Blackline

# Tests

*by Robert J. McMurray and William O. Garrett*

# Geometry

*Jurgensen*
*Brown*
*Jurgensen*

**HOUGHTON MIFFLIN COMPANY · BOSTON**

Atlanta · Dallas · Geneva, Illinois · Palo Alto · Princeton · Toronto

## About the Tests

These tests are designed to test the content and objectives of Geometry by Ray C. Jurgensen, Richard G. Brown, and John W. Jurgensen.

There are three or four tests, including a chapter test, keyed to the material in each chapter. In addition, there are cumulative tests covering the material in clusters of chapters. The cumulative tests for use after Chapters 7 and 14 are in multiple-choice format.

Each question has been assigned a suggested value so that the total number of points for each test is 100. Challenge problems appear at the end of some tests. These problems are intended to be optional and have not been included in the 100-point total.

## The Authors

**Robert J. McMurray**, Mathematics Teacher, Albuquerque (New Mexico) Public School System

**William O. Garrett**, Mathematics Teacher, Norristown Area High School, Norristown (Pennsylvania) Area School District

1992 Impression

ISBN: 0-395-57332-7

EFGHIJ-CS-99876543

# Contents

# Test 1  *Some Basic Figures*

**Directions:** Write answers in the spaces provided.

Classify each statement as true or false.

1. $\overleftrightarrow{AB}$ and $k$ are intersecting lines.

2. $\overleftrightarrow{XY}$ is the intersection of planes $P$ and $Q$.

3. $A$, $R$, and $T$ are collinear.

4. $A$, $B$, $S$, and $Y$ are coplanar.

5. Plane $P$ contains $k$.

6. $\overleftrightarrow{AB}$ intersects plane $Q$ at $S$.

7. $\overleftrightarrow{RS}$ and $\overleftrightarrow{XY}$ name the same line.

8. $A$, $R$, $S$, and $T$ are noncoplanar.

9. $A$, $R$, and $B$ are collinear.

10. A line is defined as a set of points.

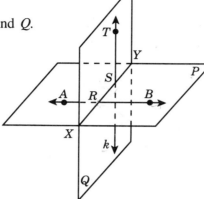

Questions 1–10

State how many points meet the requirements. For each answer write *none*, *one*, *two*, or *an unlimited number*.

11. A given distance from $P$.

12. A given distance from $P$ and on $l$.

13. On $l$ and equidistant from $P$ and $Q$.

Questions 11–13

Sketch and label the figures described. Use dashes for hidden parts.

14. vertical plane $C$

15. Vertical line $h$ intersects horizontal plane $D$ at $X$.

**Answers**

1. _____ (6)

2. _____ (6)

3. _____ (6)

4. _____ (6)

5. _____ (6)

6. _____ (6)

7. _____ (6)

8. _____ (6)

9. _____ (6)

10. _____ (6)

11. _____ (5)

12. _____ (5)

13. _____ (5)

14. (See question) _____ (6)

15. (See question) _____ (6)

16. (See question) _____ (6)

17. (See question) _____ (7)

16. Plane $M$ contains intersecting lines $r$ and $s$.

17. Planes $P$ and $Q$ contain $\overleftrightarrow{XY}$.

# Test 2   *Supplementary Test*

**Directions:** Write answers in the spaces provided.

In Questions 1–10, *B* is the midpoint of $\overline{AC}$.

1. By the Segment Addition Postulate, $DB + BE = \underline{\ ?\ }$ .

2. If $AB = 7$, then $BC = \underline{\ ?\ }$ . (numerical answer)

3. $m\angle ABD + m\angle DBC = \underline{\ ?\ }$ . (numerical answer)

4. If $DB = BE$, then *B* is the $\underline{\ ?\ }$ of $\overline{DE}$.

5. If $\overrightarrow{BF}$ bisects $\angle ABE$, then $\angle 1 \cong \angle \underline{\ ?\ }$

6. The ray opposite $\overrightarrow{BD}$ is $\underline{\ ?\ }$ .

7. $m\angle 2 + m\angle 3 = m\angle \underline{\ ?\ }$ .

8. Another name for $\overleftrightarrow{AB}$ is $\underline{\ ?\ }$ .

9. Another name for $\angle 3$ is $\angle \underline{\ ?\ }$ .

10. If $\angle 2 \cong \angle 3$, then $\overrightarrow{BE} \underline{\ ?\ } \angle FBC$.

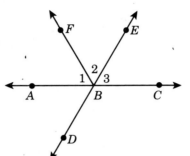

Questions 1–10

In Questions 11–15, $m\angle LHJ = 90$.

11. If $m\angle 6 = 80$, then $m\angle 5 = \underline{\ ?\ }$ .

12. $\angle 9$ appears to be a(n) $\underline{\ ?\ }$ angle.

13. $m\angle GHL = \underline{\ ?\ }$

14. If $m\angle 9 = 2x + 5$ and $m\angle 8 = 3x$, then $x = \underline{\ ?\ }$ .

15. An angle adjacent to $\angle GHK$ is $\angle \underline{\ ?\ }$ .

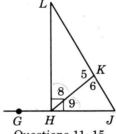

Questions 11–15

In Questions 16–18, *Q* is the midpoint of $\overline{PR}$ and *S* is the midpoint of $\overline{PQ}$.

16. $PR = \underline{\ ?\ }$

17. The coordinate of *Q* is $\underline{\ ?\ }$ .

18. $PS = \underline{\ ?\ }$

Questions 16–18

19. Which of the following does *not* represent a set of points?

   **(A)** *AB*    **(B)** $\overrightarrow{AB}$    **(C)** $\overline{AB}$    **(D)** $\overleftrightarrow{AB}$

20. Given the diagram at the right, state whether you can reach the conclusion shown.

   **a.** $\overline{AB} \cong \overline{BC}$        **b.** $\angle 1 \cong \angle 2$        **c.** $\angle 3$ is a right angle.

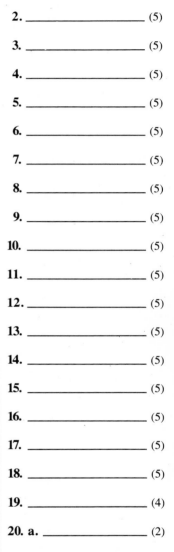

Question 20

**Answers**

1. _____ (5)
2. _____ (5)
3. _____ (5)
4. _____ (5)
5. _____ (5)
6. _____ (5)
7. _____ (5)
8. _____ (5)
9. _____ (5)
10. _____ (5)
11. _____ (5)
12. _____ (5)
13. _____ (5)
14. _____ (5)
15. _____ (5)
16. _____ (5)
17. _____ (5)
18. _____ (5)
19. _____ (4)
20. a. _____ (2)
   b. _____ (2)
   c. _____ (2)

## Test 3    *Definitions and Postulates*

**Directions:** Write answers in the spaces provided.

**Answers**

1. How many planes (0, 1, or infinitely many) can contain each set of points?

   **a.** two intersecting lines      **b.** two points
   **c.** three noncollinear points    **d.** three collinear points
   **e.** a line and a point not on the line

1. a. _____ (4)

   b. _____ (4)

   c. _____ (4)

   d. _____ (4)

   e. _____ (4)

In Questions 2–7 you may have to visualize certain lines and planes not shown in the diagram.

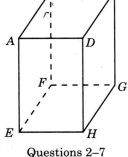

2. Name the intersection of $\overleftrightarrow{BC}$ and $\overleftrightarrow{FB}$.

3. Name the intersection of plane *ABCD* and plane *HDCG*.

4. Do $\overleftrightarrow{EG}$ and $\overleftrightarrow{DH}$ intersect?

5. Name the intersection of plane *EABF* and plane *EDCF*.

6. What part of $\overleftrightarrow{AC}$ lies in plane *ABCD*?
   **(A)** points *A* and *C* only     **(B)** $\overline{AC}$     **(C)** all of $\overleftrightarrow{AC}$

Questions 2–7

7. Are points *C*, *D*, *E*, and *G* coplanar?

8. Name a segment with endpoint at *T* and congruent to $\overline{BR}$.

9. The coordinate of the midpoint of $\overline{TL}$ is __?__ .

10. *IH* = __?__

11. The midpoint of $\overline{TJ}$ is __?__ .

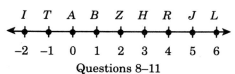

Questions 8–11

2. _____ (5)

3. _____ (5)

4. _____ (5)

5. _____ (5)

6. _____ (5)

7. _____ (5)

8. _____ (5)

9. _____ (5)

10. _____ (5)

11. _____ (5)

12. _____ (5)

13. _____ (5)

14. _____ (4)

15. _____ (4)

16. _____ (4)

17. _____ (4)

18. _____ (4)

12. Name an angle congruent to ∠*EML*.

13. __?__ bisects ∠*EMN*.

14. *m* ∠ *SMG* = __?__

15. Name a right angle.

16. ∠*LMA* is a(n) __?__ angle.

17. ∠*SMA* is a(n) __?__ angle.

18. Point *M* is called the __?__ of ∠*LMA*.

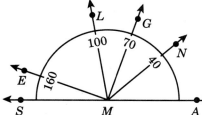

Questions 12–18

# Test 4 *Chapter 1 Test*

**Answers**

**Directions:** Write answers in the spaces provided.

In Questions 1–10, *C* is the midpoint of $\overline{RT}$ and $\angle WCV \cong \angle VCT$.

1. Name a ray opposite to $\overrightarrow{CT}$.

2. Name a ray with endpoint *S* that contains *W*.

3. Name two congruent segments.

4. Name an angle bisector.

5. $SC + CW = \underline{\ ?\ }$

6. *C* is the $\underline{\ ?\ }$ of $\angle RCS$.

7. $m\angle VCT + m\angle TCS = m\angle\ \underline{\ ?\ }$

8. If $m\angle WCT = 40$, then $m\angle WCR = \underline{\ ?\ }$.

9. If $m\angle WCT = 50$, then $m\angle VCT = \underline{\ ?\ }$.

10. Since *C* is the midpoint of $\overline{RT}$, $\overleftrightarrow{WS}\ \underline{\ ?\ }\ \overline{RT}$.

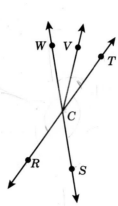

Questions 1–10

11. Name the intersection of plane *ACFD* and plane *DEF*.

12. Name a plane that contains $\overleftrightarrow{BF}$.

13. Name two planes that do not intersect.

14. Name the plane that contains $\overleftrightarrow{DE}$ and *K*.

15. Name three lines shown that intersect at point *D*.

16. Are points *K*, *L*, and *M* collinear?

17. Are points *K*, *L*, and *M* coplanar?

18. Name the intersection of $\overleftrightarrow{DE}$ and plane *FDAC*.

Questions 11–18

19. If $\overrightarrow{NQ}$ bisects $\angle RNP$, then $\angle QNP \cong \underline{\ ?\ }$.

20. If $\overrightarrow{RN}$ bisects $\angle SRQ$ and $m\angle 2 = 55$, then $m\angle 1 = \underline{\ ?\ }$.

21. Name a right angle.

22. Name an angle that appears to be obtuse.

23. Name a straight angle.

24. Name an acute angle with vertex at *N*.

25. Name an angle adjacent to $\angle MNQ$.

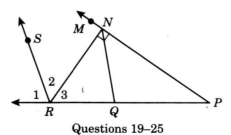

Questions 19–25

| Answers | |
|---|---|
| 1. _____ | (2) |
| 2. _____ | (2) |
| 3. _____ | (2) |
| 4. _____ | (2) |
| 5. _____ | (2) |
| 6. _____ | (2) |
| 7. _____ | (2) |
| 8. _____ | (2) |
| 9. _____ | (2) |
| 10. _____ | (2) |
| 11. _____ | (3) |
| 12. _____ | (3) |
| 13. _____ | (3) |
| 14. _____ | (3) |
| 15. _____ | (3) |
| 16. _____ | (3) |
| 17. _____ | (3) |
| 18. _____ | (3) |
| 19. _____ | (3) |
| 20. _____ | (3) |
| 21. _____ | (2) |
| 22. _____ | (2) |
| 23. _____ | (2) |
| 24. _____ | (2) |
| 25. _____ | (2) |

*(continued)*

## TEST 4 *(continued)*

In Questions 26–30, $F$ is the midpoint of $\overline{AD}$. Classify each statement as *true, false,* or *cannot be determined.*

**26.** $\angle 1$ and $\angle BFD$ are adjacent angles.

**27.** $\angle CFD$ is a right angle.

**28.** $AF = FD$

**29.** $\overline{AF} \cong \overline{FB}$

**30.** $\angle 1 \cong \angle 2$

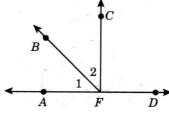

Questions 26–30

Classify each statement as true or false.

**31.** If two lines intersect, then they intersect in exactly one point.

**32.** It is possible for two planes to intersect in exactly one point.

**33.** Three points always lie in exactly one plane.

**34.** If $C$ is the midpoint of $\overline{XY}$, then $C$ must be between $X$ and $Y$.

**35.** A postulate is a statement that is accepted without proof.

**36.** A plane is defined as an infinite set of points in a flat surface.

**37.** Congruent angles are angles that have equal measures.

**38.** Which of the following sets of points are contained in exactly one plane? (More than one answer is possible.)

   **(A)** three collinear points    **(D)** a line and a point not on the line
   **(B)** two intersecting lines    **(E)** three noncollinear points
   **(C)** two points          **(F)** one point

**39.** If $AB = 3x - 5$, $BC = x + 2$, and $AC = 13$, then $x = \underline{\ ?\ }$.

**40.** If $m\angle 1 = 5x + 7$ and $m\angle 2 = 7x + 17$, then $x = \underline{\ ?\ }$.

**Answers**

26. _____ (2)

27. _____ (2)

28. _____ (2)

29. _____ (2)

30. _____ (2)

31. _____ (3)

32. _____ (3)

33. _____ (3)

34. _____ (3)

35. _____ (3)

36. _____ (3)

37. _____ (3)

38. _____ (3)

39. _____ (3)

40. _____ (3)

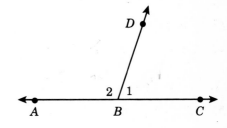

Questions 39, 40

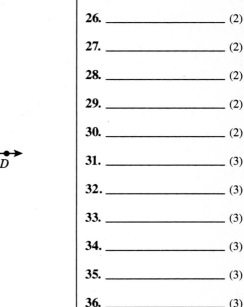

**CHALLENGE (Optional)**
Excluding straight angles, how many angles are shown in the figure?

**ANSWER**

_____

# Test 5   *Using Deductive Reasoning*

**Lessons 2-1 through 2-3**

**Directions:** Write answers in the spaces provided.

For each conditional, underline the hypothesis once and the conclusion twice.

1. If Melissa practices the flute, then she plays well.

2. The lake begins to freeze only if the temperature drops below 0°C.

3. $S$ is the midpoint of $\overline{RT}$ implies $RS = ST$.

4. The car will not start if the battery is discharged.

Provide a counterexample to show that each statement is false.

5. If the sum of two integers is even, then the integers are even.

6. An angle is an obtuse angle if its measure is greater than 90.

Tell whether the converse of each conditional is true or false.

7. If an integer is greater than 10, then it is a positive integer.

8. An angle is a right angle if its measure is 90.

**9–12.** Complete the following proof by supplying the letter of the reason that justifies each statement in the proof.

(A) Addition Prop. of =    (F) Subtraction Prop. of =
(B) Multiplication Prop. of =    (G) Midpoint Theorem
(C) Definition of midpoint    (H) Reflexive Prop.
(D) Segment Addition Postulate    (I) Symmetric Prop.
(E) Substitution Prop.    (J) Transitive Prop.

Given: $AC = BD$
Prove: $AB = CD$
Proof:

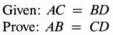 

| Statements | Reasons |
|---|---|
| 1. $AC = BD$ | 1. Given |
| 2. $AB + BC = AC$; $BC + CD = BD$ | 2. Answer on line 9 |
| 3. $AB + BC = BC + CD$ | 3. Answer on line 10 |
| 4. $BC = BC$ | 4. Answer on line 11 |
| 5. $AB = CD$ | 5. Answer on line 12 |

In Questions 13–16, $R$ is the midpoint of $\overline{QT}$, $S$ is the midpoint of $\overline{RT}$, $\overrightarrow{RX}$ bisects $\angle WRZ$, and $\overrightarrow{RY}$ bisects $\angle XRZ$.

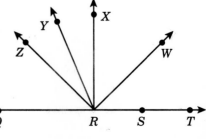

13. By the Midpoint Theorem, $RS = \frac{1}{2}\,\underline{\ ?\ }$.

14. If $QT = 26$, then $QR = \underline{\ ?\ }$ and $ST = \underline{\ ?\ }$.

15. By the Angle Bisector Theorem, $m\angle WRX = \frac{1}{2}m\angle\underline{\ ?\ }$.

16. If $m\angle YRZ = 26$, then $m\angle XRZ = \underline{\ ?\ }$ and $m\angle WRZ = \underline{\ ?\ }$.

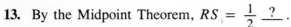

Questions 13–16

**Answers**

1. (See question) ____ (10)
2. (See question) ____ (10)
3. (See question) ____ (10)
4. (See question) ____ (10)
5. _____ (5)
6. _____ (5)
7. _____ (5)
8. _____ (5)
9. _____ (5)
10. _____ (5)
11. _____ (5)
12. _____ (5)
13. _____ (5)
14. _____ (5)
15. _____ (5)
16. _____ (5)

# Test 6   *Supplementary Test*

**Directions:** Write answers in the spaces provided.

In Questions 1–16, write the letter of the reason that justifies each statement.

**(A)** Addition Prop. of =
**(B)** Multiplication Prop. of =
**(C)** Segment Addition Postulate
**(D)** Angle Addition Postulate
**(E)** Definition of midpoint
**(F)** Definition of angle bisector
**(G)** Vertical angles are congruent.
**(H)** If two lines are perpendicular, then they form congruent adjacent angles.
**(I)** If two lines form congruent adjacent angles, then they are perpendicular.
**(J)** Midpoint Theorem
**(K)** Angle Bisector Theorem
**(L)** Reflexive Prop.
**(M)** Transitive Prop.
**(N)** Definition of segment bisector
**(O)** Definition of right angle
**(P)** Definition of perpendicular lines

**Answers**

1. _____ (5)
2. _____ (5)
3. _____ (5)
4. _____ (5)
5. _____ (5)
6. _____ (5)
7. _____ (5)
8. _____ (5)
9. _____ (5)
10. _____ (5)
11. _____ (5)
12. _____ (5)
13. _____ (5)
14. _____ (5)
15. _____ (5)
16. _____ (5)
17. _____ (5)
18. _____ (5)
19. _____ (5)
20. _____ (5)

Given: $X$ is the midpoint of $\overline{AB}$; $\overrightarrow{XE}$ bisects $\angle CXB$.

1. $CX + XD = CD$
2. $AX = XB$
3. $\angle AXC \cong \angle DXB$
4. $m \angle 1 = m \angle 2$
5. $m \angle 1 = \frac{1}{2} m \angle CXB$
6. $XE = XE$
7. $AX = \frac{1}{2} AB$
8. $m \angle AXE + m \angle EXB = 180$

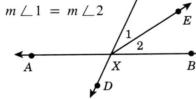

Questions 1–8

Given: $m \angle 3 = m \angle 4$; $\overline{MG} \perp \overline{KL}$; $KI = IL$, $IL = MI$

9. $\angle 5 \cong \angle 6$
10. $KI = MI$
11. $I$ is the midpoint of $\overline{KL}$.
12. $\angle 5 \cong \angle LIG$
13. $2 \cdot KI = 2 \cdot IL$
14. $\angle 5$ is a right angle.
15. $\overrightarrow{IJ}$ bisects $\angle MIL$.
16. $m \angle 3 + m \angle 4 = m \angle MIL$

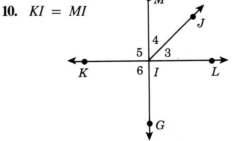

Questions 9–16

In Questions 17–20, $\overline{DE} \perp \overline{EH}$, $m \angle ABH = 50$, and $\overrightarrow{BF}$ bisects $\angle CBE$.

17. Name an angle supplementary to $\angle DBF$.
18. Name a pair of vertical angles.
19. Name two complementary angles.
20. $m \angle EBF = \underline{\phantom{?}}$ *(numerical answer)*

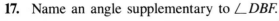

Questions 17–20

---

# Test 7 *Theorems about Angles and Perpendicular Lines*

**Directions:** Write answers in the spaces provided.

1. Vertical angles are __?__ .

2. A complement of an acute angle is a(n) __?__ angle.

3. A supplement of a right angle is a(n) __?__ angle.

4. A supplement of an acute angle is a(n) __?__ angle.

5. Find the measure of a supplement of an angle with measure 75.

6. If $m \angle A = 3y$, and $\angle A$ and $\angle B$ are complementary angles, find the measure of $\angle B$ in terms of $y$.

In Questions 7–11, $\overrightarrow{GD} \perp \overleftrightarrow{EB}$.

7. Name a right angle.

8. Name two complementary angles.

9. Name two congruent adjacent angles.

10. Name a supplement of $\angle EGA$.

11. If $m \angle 5 = 40$, then:
   (a) $m \angle 2 = $ __?__ and (b) $m \angle 3 = $ __?__ .

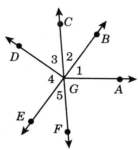

Questions 7–11

12. If $\angle 7$ is supplementary to $\angle 8$ and $\angle 9$ is supplementary to $\angle 8$, what can you conclude about $\angle 7$ and $\angle 9$?

13. If $\angle 5$ is complementary to $\angle 3$ and $\angle 3 \cong \angle 4$, what can you conclude about $\angle 5$ and $\angle 4$?

14. Complete the proof.

   Given: $\overline{ST} \perp \overline{TU}$; $\angle RST$ is a right angle;
   $\qquad \angle 2 \cong \angle 3$
   Prove: $\angle 1 \cong \angle 4$
   Proof:

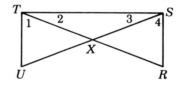

**Answers**

1. _____ (5)

2. _____ (5)

3. _____ (5)

4. _____ (5)

5. _____ (5)

6. _____ (5)

7. _____ (5)

8. _____ (5)

9. _____ (5)

10. _____ (5)

11. a. _____ (5)

   b. _____ (5)

12. _____ (5)

13. _____ (5)

14. (See proof) _____ (30)

| Statements | Reasons |
|---|---|
| 1. $\angle RST$ is a right angle. | 1. Given |
| 2. $\overline{SR} \perp \overline{ST}$ | 2. _____ |
| 3. $\angle 3$ and $\angle 4$ are comp. $\angle$s. | 3. _____ |
| 4. $\overline{ST} \perp \overline{TU}$ | 4. _____ |
| 5. $\angle 1$ and $\angle 2$ are comp. $\angle$s. | 5. _____ |
| 6. $\angle 2 \cong \angle 3$ | 6. _____ |
| 7. $\angle 1 \cong \angle 4$ | 7. _____ |

# Test 8 *Chapter 2 Test*

**Directions:** Write answers in the spaces provided.

For each conditional, underline the hypothesis once and the conclusion twice.

1. If Michele plays her viola, then she must put rosin on her bow.

2. Class rank will be determined only if final exams are completed.

3. $3x + 1 = 1$ implies $x = 0$.

Write the letter of the converse of each conditional.

4. If you go, then I stay.

5. I go if you stay.

6. I go only if you stay.

(A) If I go, then you stay.

(B) If you stay, then I go.

(C) If I stay, then you go.

(D) If you go, then I stay.

Classify each statement as true or false.

7. Definitions may be used as reasons in a proof.

8. A statement in the form *If p and q, then r* is a biconditional.

9. The converse of a true conditional is always true.

10. The converse of a false conditional is always false.

11. Perpendicular lines form congruent adjacent angles.

12. Two angles complementary to the same angle are complementary to each other.

13. Two angles congruent to the same angle are congruent to each other.

14. The Substitution Property and the Transitive Property may always be used interchangeably.

Draw a counterexample to show that each statement is false.

15. Vertical angles are never supplementary.

16. Two lines always intersect.

In Questions 17–20, $\overleftrightarrow{AD} \perp \overleftrightarrow{FC}$ and $m \angle 1 = 38$.

17. $m \angle ADF = \underline{\ ?\ }$

18. $m \angle EDC = \underline{\ ?\ }$

19. $m \angle CDB = \underline{\ ?\ }$

20. $m \angle ADB = \underline{\ ?\ }$

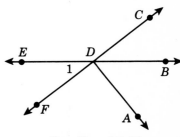

Questions 17–20

**Answers**

1. (See question) ___ (3)

2. (See question) ___ (3)

3. (See question) ___ (3)

4. _____ (3)

5. _____ (3)

6. _____ (3)

7. _____ (3)

8. _____ (3)

9. _____ (3)

10. _____ (3)

11. _____ (3)

12. _____ (3)

13. _____ (3)

14. _____ (3)

15. (See question) ___ (3)

16. (See question) ___ (3)

17. _____ (2)

18. _____ (2)

19. _____ (2)

20. _____ (3)

*(continued)*

NAME _____ DATE _____ SCORE _____

## Test 8 *(continued)*

In Questions 21–23, $\overline{OT} \perp \overline{YS}$. Use the given information to find the value of $x$.

**21.** $m \angle 1 = 3x; \; m \angle 4 = x + 30$

**22.** $m \angle 3 = 2x + 20; \; m \angle 4 = x + 10$

**23.** $m \angle 1 = x + 1; \; m \angle VOS = 4x - 6$

**24.** If $m \angle 4 = y$, then find the measure of $\angle YOR$ in terms of $y$.

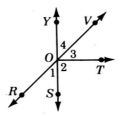

Questions 21–24

Write the letter of the reason that justifies each statement.

**(A)** Definition of complementary angles

**(B)** Definition of supplementary angles

**(C)** Definition of perpendicular lines

**(D)** Angle Addition Postulate

**(E)** If two lines are perpendicular, then they form congruent adjacent angles.

**(F)** If two lines form congruent adjacent angles, then the lines are perpendicular.

**(G)** If the exterior sides of two adjacent acute angles are perpendicular, then the angles are complementary.

**(H)** Definition of angle bisector

**(I)** Angle Bisector Theorem

**(J)** Definition of right angle

**(K)** Segment Addition Postulate

**25.** If $\overline{FB} \perp \overline{AC}$, then $\angle 7$ is complementary to $\angle EBC$.

**26.** If $m \angle 8 = 90$, then $\angle 8$ is a right angle.

**27.** If $\angle 8$ is a right angle, then $\overline{FB} \perp \overline{AC}$.

**28.** If $\overrightarrow{BE}$ bisects $\angle FBD$, then $\angle 7 \cong \angle 6$.

**29.** $m \angle ABD + m \angle DBC = 180$

**30.** If $\overline{FB} \perp \overline{AC}$, then $\angle 8 \cong \angle FBC$.

**31.** If $m \angle FBD + m \angle 5 = 90$, then $\angle FBD$ is complementary to $\angle 5$.

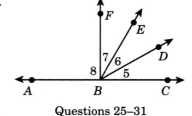

Questions 25–31

**32.** Write a two-column proof.

Given: $\overrightarrow{KH}$ bisects $\angle GKJ$.
Prove: $\angle 9 \cong \angle 10$
Proof:

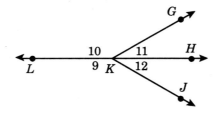

### Answers

21. _____ (3)

22. _____ (3)

23. _____ (3)

24. _____ (3)

25. _____ (3)

26. _____ (3)

27. _____ (3)

28. _____ (3)

29. _____ (3)

30. _____ (3)

31. _____ (3)

32. (See proof) _____ (10)

### CHALLENGE (Optional)

Given:
  $\angle B$ is a comp. of $\angle A$.
  $\angle C$ is a supp. of $\angle B$.
  $\angle D$ is a supp. of $\angle C$.
  $\angle E$ is a comp. of $\angle D$.
  $\angle F$ is a comp. of $\angle E$.
  $\angle G$ is a supp. of $\angle F$.

Then $\angle G \cong \; \underline{\;?\;}$

### ANSWER

_____

# Test 9  *When Lines and Planes Are Parallel*

**Answers**

**Directions:** Write answers in the spaces provided.

1. If plane *ABCDE* ∥ plane *PQRST*, then $\overline{ED}$ ∥ _?_ .

2. If plane *AETP* ∥ plane *BCRQ*, then $\overline{AE}$ ∥ _?_ .

3. If $\overline{PQ}$ ∥ $\overline{SR}$ and $\overline{DC}$ ∥ $\overline{SR}$, then $\overline{PQ}$ ∥ _?_ .

4. $\overleftrightarrow{ED}$ and $\overleftrightarrow{BQ}$ are called _?_ lines.

5. Is $\overleftrightarrow{ET}$ a transversal for $\overleftrightarrow{ED}$ and $\overleftrightarrow{TP}$?

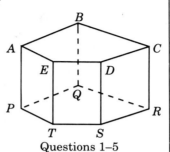

Questions 1–5

6. Name a pair of alternate interior angles.

7. Name a pair of corresponding angles.

8. Name a pair of same-side interior angles.

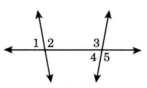

Questions 6–8

Given $\overleftrightarrow{AB}$ ∥ $\overleftrightarrow{CD}$, state whether the given angles are *congruent* or *supplementary*. If no conclusion can be reached, write *no conclusion*.

9. ∠1 and ∠4    10. ∠5 and ∠2

11. ∠3 and ∠6    12. ∠4 and ∠2

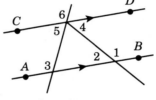

Questions 9–12

Given *l* ∥ *m*, find the measure of each angle.

13. $m\angle 1 = $ _?_

14. $m\angle 2 = $ _?_

15. $m\angle 3 = $ _?_

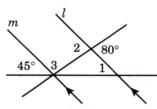

Questions 13–15

Complete each statement with $\overline{WT}$ ∥ $\overline{RS}$, $\overline{WR}$ ∥ $\overline{VS}$, $\overline{RV}$ ∥ $\overline{ST}$, or *no conclusion is possible.*

16. If ∠1 ≅ ∠4, then _?_ .

17. If ∠*VRS* is supp. to ∠*TSR*, then _?_ .

18. If ∠4 ≅ ∠12, then _?_ .

19. If ∠6 ≅ ∠8, then _?_ .

20. If ∠2 ≅ ∠5, then _?_ .

21. If $\overline{WR}$ ⊥ $\overline{WT}$ and $\overline{VS}$ ⊥ $\overline{WT}$, then _?_ .

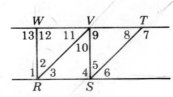

Questions 16–21

1. _____ (5)
2. _____ (5)
3. _____ (5)
4. _____ (5)
5. _____ (5)
6. _____ (4)
7. _____ (4)
8. _____ (4)
9. _____ (5)
10. _____ (5)
11. _____ (5)
12. _____ (5)
13. _____ (4)
14. _____ (4)
15. _____ (5)
16. _____ (5)
17. _____ (5)
18. _____ (5)
19. _____ (5)
20. _____ (5)
21. _____ (5)

NAME _____ DATE _____ SCORE _____

# Test 10 *Supplementary Test*

**Directions:** Write answers in the spaces provided.

**Answers**

Write the letter of the name that best describes each triangle.

(A) Scalene acute triangle       (E) Isosceles right triangle
(B) Scalene right triangle        (F) Isosceles obtuse triangle
(C) Scalene obtuse triangle      (G) Equilateral triangle
(D) Isosceles acute triangle

1. $\triangle ABC$      2. $\triangle BCD$
3. $\triangle BDE$      4. $\triangle BCE$
5. $\triangle CEF$      6. $\triangle ACF$

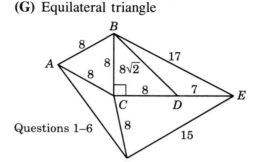

Questions 1–6

1. _____ (5)
2. _____ (5)
3. _____ (5)
4. _____ (5)
5. _____ (5)
6. _____ (5)
7. _____ (5)
8. _____ (5)
9. _____ (5)
10. _____ (5)
11. _____ (5)
12. _____ (5)
13. _____ (5)
14. _____ (5)
15. _____ (6)
16. _____ (6)
17. _____ (6)
18. _____ (6)
19. _____ (6)

7. If $m \angle 2 = 30$ and $m \angle 6 = 80$, find $m \angle 3$.
8. If $m \angle 1 = 160$ and $m \angle 3 = 70$, find $m \angle 6$.
9. If $m \angle 4 = 110$ and $m \angle 5 = 100$, find $m \angle 1$.
10. If $m \angle 2 = 40$ and $m \angle 3 = m \angle 6$, find $m \angle 3$.
11. If $m \angle 6 = 90$, find $m \angle 1 + m \angle 4$.

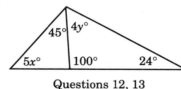

Questions 7–11

12. Find the value of $x$.
13. Find the value of $y$.

Questions 12, 13

14. Find the measure of one exterior angle of an equiangular triangle.

15. The measure of the largest angle of a triangle is twice the measure of the smallest angle and 20 more than the measure of the third angle. Find the measure of each angle.

16. The measure of one interior angle of a regular polygon is 140. Find the number of sides.

17. Find the measure of one interior angle of a regular polygon with 20 sides.

18. Find the measure of one exterior angle of a regular polygon with 12 sides.

19. Five of the angles of a convex hexagon have measures 112, 100, 90, 160, and 115. Find the measure of the sixth angle.

# Test 11  *Applying Parallel Lines to Polygons*  | Lessons 3-4 through 3-6 |

**Directions:** Write answers in the spaces provided.

**Answers**

In Questions 1–6, $\overline{AB} \perp \overline{BC}$.

1. $m \angle 1 = \underline{\phantom{?}}$
2. $m \angle 2 = \underline{\phantom{?}}$
3. $m \angle 3 = \underline{\phantom{?}}$
4. $m \angle 4 = \underline{\phantom{?}}$
5. $m \angle 5 = \underline{\phantom{?}}$
6. $m \angle 6 = \underline{\phantom{?}}$

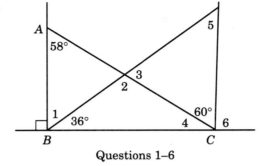

Questions 1–6

In Questions 7–11, $\overline{XY} \perp \overline{YC}$.

7. Name an isosceles triangle that is not equilateral.
8. Name a right triangle.
9. Name a scalene triangle.
10. Name an acute triangle.
11. Name an exterior angle of $\triangle XYC$.

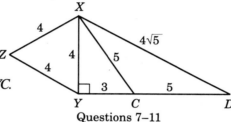

Questions 7–11

12. Find the sum of the measures of the interior angles of a convex hexagon.

13. Find the sum of the measures of the exterior angles, one at each vertex, of a convex octagon.

14. The measures of the three angles of a triangle are represented by $x$, $2x$, and $x + 60$. Find the numerical measure of each angle.

15. Find the measure of each exterior angle of a regular polygon with 15 sides.

16. The measure of one interior angle of a regular polygon is 144. Find the number of sides.

Accept the two statements as given information. State a conclusion based on deductive reasoning. If no conclusion can be reached, write *none*.

17. All birds have wings.
    The Spruce Goose has wings.

18. $\triangle ABC$ is not acute.
    $\triangle ABC$ is not obtuse.

Use inductive reasoning to determine the next *two* numbers in each sequence.

19. 1, 2, 5, 10, 17, . . .

20. 96, 48, 24, 12, 6, . . .

1. _____ (5)
2. _____ (5)
3. _____ (5)
4. _____ (5)
5. _____ (5)
6. _____ (5)
7. _____ (4)
8. _____ (4)
9. _____ (4)
10. _____ (4)
11. _____ (4)
12. _____ (6)
13. _____ (6)
14. _____ (6)
15. _____ (6)
16. _____ (6)
17. _____ (5)
18. _____ (5)
19. _____ (5)
20. _____ (5)

# Test 12   *Chapter 3 Test*

**Answers**

**Directions:** Write answers in the spaces provided.

Given *a* ∥ *b*, state whether the given angles must be *congruent* or *supplementary*. If no conclusion can be reached, write *no conclusion*.

1.  ∠5 and ∠18
2.  ∠8 and ∠10
3.  ∠2 and ∠10
4.  ∠4 and ∠14
5.  ∠12 and ∠7
6.  ∠2 and ∠15

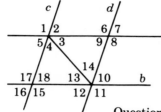

Questions 1–11

Write the letter of the choice that best completes each statement. Use the figure above.

7.  If ∠3 ≅ ∠13, then __?__ .
8.  If ∠7 ≅ ∠18, then __?__ .
9.  If ∠5 and ∠8 are supplementary, then __?__ .
10. If ∠1 ≅ ∠6 and ∠6 and ∠16 are supplementary, then __?__ .
11. If ∠16 ≅ ∠10, then __?__ .

**(A)** *a* ∥ *b*
**(B)** *c* ∥ *d*
**(C)** *a* ∥ *b* and *c* ∥ *d*
**(D)** no conclusion

Complete.

12. *m* ∠1 = __?__
13. *m* ∠2 = __?__
14. *m* ∠3 = __?__
15. *m* ∠4 = __?__
16. *m* ∠5 = __?__

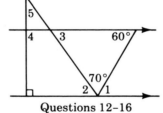

Questions 12–16

Use the diagram and the given information to find the value of *x*.

17. *m* ∠6 = *x*;  *m* ∠8 = *x* − 20
18. *m* ∠7 = *x*;  *m* ∠9 = 3*x* + 20
19. *m* ∠8 = 3*x* − 8;
    *m* ∠7 = 2*x* + 10
20. *m* ∠6 = 8*x* − 9;
    *m* ∠7 = 3*x*

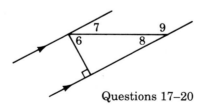

Questions 17–20

| | |
|---|---|
| 1. _____ | (2) |
| 2. _____ | (2) |
| 3. _____ | (2) |
| 4. _____ | (2) |
| 5. _____ | (2) |
| 6. _____ | (2) |
| 7. _____ | (3) |
| 8. _____ | (3) |
| 9. _____ | (3) |
| 10. _____ | (3) |
| 11. _____ | (3) |
| 12. _____ | (2) |
| 13. _____ | (2) |
| 14. _____ | (2) |
| 15. _____ | (2) |
| 16. _____ | (2) |
| 17. _____ | (4) |
| 18. _____ | (4) |
| 19. _____ | (4) |
| 20. _____ | (4) |

*(continued)*

**SHEET 14**

# Test 12 (continued)

Complete each statement with the word *always*, *sometimes*, or *never*.

**21.** If △*AEF* is equiangular, then *m* ∠*E* is _?_ 50.

**22.** In a triangle there can _?_ be at most one right angle or one obtuse angle.

**23.** If two parallel lines are cut by a transversal, then the alternate interior angles are _?_ supplementary.

**24.** In a plane, two lines perpendicular to the same line are _?_ parallel.

**25.** The acute angles of a right triangle are _?_ congruent.

**26.** A scalene triangle _?_ has two congruent sides.

**27.** Find the sum of the measures of the interior angles of a polygon with 7 sides.

**28.** Find the measure of one interior angle of a regular polygon with 30 sides.

**29.** Find the measure of one exterior angle of a regular polygon with 45 sides.

Accept the two statements as given information. State a conclusion based on deductive reasoning. If no conclusion can be reached, write *none*.

**30.** ∠*A* is supplementary to ∠*B*.    **31.** All equiangular triangles are acute.
∠*B* is supplementary to ∠*C*.        △*ABC* is acute.

Use inductive reasoning to predict the next *two* numbers in each sequence.

**32.** 1, 11, 20, 28, . . .      **33.** 34, 36, 18, 20, 10, . . .

**34.** Write a two-column proof.

Given: *a* ∥ *b*; ∠1 ≅ ∠2
Prove: ∠3 ≅ ∠4
Proof:

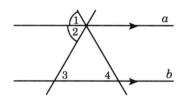

## Answers

21. _____ (2)

22. _____ (2)

23. _____ (2)

24. _____ (2)

25. _____ (2)

26. _____ (2)

27. _____ (3)

28. _____ (3)

29. _____ (3)

30. _____ (4)

31. _____ (4)

32. _____ (4)

33. _____ (4)

34. (See proof) _____ (10)

## CHALLENGE (Optional)

*ABCDE* and *HIJKL* are regular pentagons, *AEFGHL* is a regular hexagon.

∠*ABK* ≅ ∠*LKB*

Find *m* ∠*ABK*.

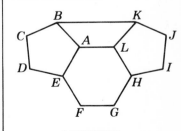

**ANSWER**

# Test 13    *Cumulative Test, Chapters 1–3*

**Answers**

**Directions:** Write answers in the spaces provided.

Complete each statement with the word *always*, *sometimes*, or *never*.

1. Collinear points are __?__ on one line.

2. Two noncoplanar lines __?__ intersect.

3. A bisector of a segment __?__ intersects the segment at its midpoint.

4. If two angles are complementary, then they are __?__ adjacent angles.

5. If a triangle is isosceles, then it is __?__ a right triangle.

6. Vertical angles are __?__ congruent.

7. If an angle is acute, then its supplement is __?__ acute.

8. If a polygon is equilateral, then it is __?__ a regular polygon.

9. If two lines form congruent adjacent angles, then the lines are __?__ perpendicular.

10. If two planes intersect, then they are __?__ parallel.

11. If two lines are parallel, then they are __?__ coplanar.

12. The sum of the measures of the exterior angles of a convex polygon, one at each vertex, is __?__ equal to the sum of the measures of the interior angles of that polygon.

13. If a triangle has one acute angle and one right angle, then the third angle is __?__ obtuse.

14. A definition can __?__ be written as a biconditional.

15. A conclusion based on inductive reasoning is __?__ true.

16. Two lines perpendicular to the same line are __?__ parallel.

Given the diagram, state whether you can reach the conclusion shown.

17. $AF + FC = AC$

18. $\overline{AE} \cong \overline{ED}$

19. $\angle EGA \cong \angle HGB$

20. $\overline{HA}$ bisects $\overline{DC}$.

21. $\angle EAF$ and $\angle BAF$ are complementary.

22. $\overrightarrow{AH}$ bisects $\angle DAC$.

23. $\angle AFB \cong \angle BFC$

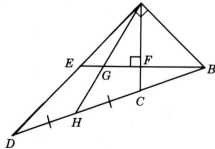

Questions 17–23

| | |
|---|---|
| 1. _____ | (1) |
| 2. _____ | (1) |
| 3. _____ | (1) |
| 4. _____ | (1) |
| 5. _____ | (1) |
| 6. _____ | (1) |
| 7. _____ | (1) |
| 8. _____ | (1) |
| 9. _____ | (1) |
| 10. _____ | (1) |
| 11. _____ | (1) |
| 12. _____ | (1) |
| 13. _____ | (1) |
| 14. _____ | (1) |
| 15. _____ | (1) |
| 16. _____ | (2) |
| 17. _____ | (2) |
| 18. _____ | (2) |
| 19. _____ | (2) |
| 20. _____ | (2) |
| 21. _____ | (2) |
| 22. _____ | (2) |
| 23. _____ | (2) |

*(continued)*

## Test 13 *(continued)*

In each exercise some information is given. Use this information to name the lines that must be parallel. If there are no such lines, write *none*.

**24.** $\angle 4 \cong \angle 11$

**25.** $\angle 9 \cong \angle 19$

**26.** $\angle 7$ and $\angle 19$ are supplementary.

**27.** $\angle 10 \cong \angle 20$

**28.** $m\angle 4 + m\angle 5 + m\angle 9 = 180$

Given $d \parallel e$, state whether you can reach the conclusion shown.

**29.** $\angle 2 \cong \angle 12$

**30.** $\angle 15$ and $\angle 16$ are supplementary.

**31.** $\angle 9 \cong \angle 12$

**32.** $\angle 5 \cong \angle 10$

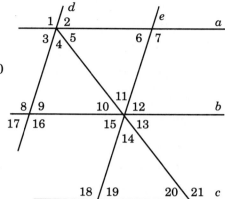

Questions 24–32

Complete each statement.

**33.** The sum of the measures of the angles of a triangle is __?__ .

**34.** The measure of each angle of an equiangular triangle is __?__ .

**35.** A polygon that has 10 sides is called a(n) __?__ .

**36.** The measure of an exterior angle of a triangle is equal to the sum of the measures of its __?__ interior angles.

**37.** An angle whose measure is 180 is called a(n) __?__ angle.

**38.** If the sum of the measures of two angles is 90, then the angles are called __?__ angles.

**39.** Reasoning that involves drawing conclusions based on past observations is called __?__ reasoning.

**40.** If two planes intersect, then their intersection is a __?__ .

**41.** Noncoplanar lines are called __?__ lines.

**42.** If two lines intersect, then their intersection is a __?__ .

**43.** The acute angles of a right triangle are __?__ .

24. _____ (2)

25. _____ (2)

26. _____ (2)

27. _____ (2)

28. _____ (2)

29. _____ (2)

30. _____ (2)

31. _____ (2)

32. _____ (2)

33. _____ (2)

34. _____ (2)

35. _____ (2)

36. _____ (2)

37. _____ (2)

38. _____ (2)

39. _____ (2)

40. _____ (2)

41. _____ (2)

42. _____ (2)

43. _____ (2)

*(continued)*

## Test 13 *(continued)*

Write the name or statement of the definition, postulate, or theorem that justifies each statement.

Given: $X$ is the midpoint of $\overline{BD}$;
$\overline{EB} \perp \overline{BC}$

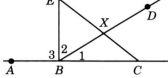

44. $m\angle ABD + m\angle 1 = 180$ _____

45. $BX = \frac{1}{2}BD$ _____

46. $\angle 3$ is a right angle. _____

47. $\angle 3 \cong \angle EBC$ _____

48. $\angle EXB \cong \angle DXC$ _____

49. Use the conditional: Two angles are congruent if they are right angles.

    **a.** Write the hypothesis. _____

    **b.** Write the conclusion. _____

    **c.** Write the converse. _____

_____

50. The sum of the measures of four angles of a pentagon is 405. Find the measure of the fifth angle.

51. Find the measure of one exterior angle of a regular octagon.

52. Given a triangle with two congruent angles that each measure 50, find the measure of the third angle.

53. Write a two-column proof.

    Given: $\overline{AB} \perp \overline{BE}$; $\overline{CD} \perp \overline{BE}$;
    $\overline{AD} \parallel \overline{CE}$
    Prove: $\angle A \cong \angle C$
    Proof:

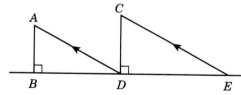

**Answers**

44. __(See question)__ (2)

45. __(See question)__ (2)

46. __(See question)__ (2)

47. __(See question)__ (2)

48. __(See question)__ (2)

49. a. __(See question)__ (2)

   b. __(See question)__ (2)

   c. __(See question)__ (2)

50. _____ (2)

51. _____ (2)

52. _____ (2)

53. __(See proof)__ (7)

# Test 14 Corresponding Parts in a Congruence

**Answers**

**Directions:** Write answers in the spaces provided.

Given that $\triangle JRX \cong \triangle QSY$, complete each statement.

**1.** $\overline{RX} \cong$ __?__  **2.** $\angle J \cong$ __?__  **3.** $\triangle RJX \cong$ __?__

Using the given information, decide whether the two triangles must be congruent. If so, **(a)** write the congruence and **(b)** name the postulate used. If no congruence can be deduced, write *none* for both (a) and (b).

**4.**
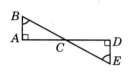

**5.**
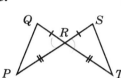

**6.**
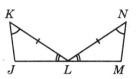

**7.** $\angle A$ and $\angle D$ are right angles; $\overline{AB} \cong \overline{DE}$; $\overline{AC} \cong \overline{DC}$

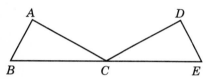

**8.** $\overline{GI} \perp \overline{FH}$; $\angle FGI \cong \angle HGI$

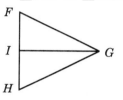

**9.** $\overline{OP} \cong \overline{QR}$; $\overline{OR} \cong \overline{QP}$

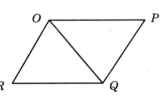

**10.** $\angle T \cong \angle V$; $\overline{TU} \cong \overline{VU}$

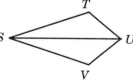

In Questions 11–18, write *before* if the statement can be justified before the triangles are proved congruent and write *after* if the statement can be justified only after the triangles are proved congruent.

Given: $D$ is the midpoint of $\overline{AB}$; $\overline{CD} \perp \overline{AB}$

**11.** $\overline{AC} \cong \overline{BC}$  **12.** $\angle 1 \cong \angle 2$

**13.** $\angle 3 \cong \angle 4$  **14.** $\overline{AD} \cong \overline{BD}$

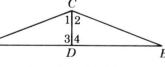

Questions 11–14

Given: $\overline{PQ} \parallel \overline{SR}$; $\overline{PQ} \cong \overline{SR}$

**15.** $\angle 2 \cong \angle 4$  **16.** $\angle P \cong \angle R$

**17.** $\angle 1 \cong \angle 3$  **18.** $\overline{PS} \cong \overline{RQ}$

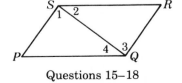

Questions 15–18

1. _____ (4)
2. _____ (4)
3. _____ (4)
4. a. _____ (4)
   b. _____ (4)
5. a. _____ (4)
   b. _____ (4)
6. a. _____ (4)
   b. _____ (4)
7. a. _____ (4)
   b. _____ (4)
8. a. _____ (4)
   b. _____ (4)
9. a. _____ (4)
   b. _____ (4)
10. a. _____ (4)
    b. _____ (4)
11. _____ (4)
12. _____ (4)
13. _____ (4)
14. _____ (4)
15. _____ (4)
16. _____ (4)
17. _____ (4)
18. _____ (4)

NAME _____ DATE _____ SCORE _____

# Test 15  *Some Theorems Based on Congruent Triangles*

**Directions:** Write answers in the spaces provided.

Questions 1, 2

1. In $\triangle PQR$, name:
   a. the hypotenuse  b. the legs

2. In $\triangle XYZ$, name:
   a. a base angle   b. the base
   c. the vertex angle  d. a leg

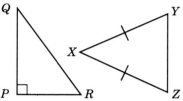

3. If $\overline{AD} \cong \overline{BD}$, name two congruent angles.

4. If $\overline{BC} \cong \overline{BD}$, name two congruent angles.

5. If $\angle A \cong \angle 4$, name two congruent segments.

6. If $\angle 2 \cong \angle 3$, name two congruent segments.

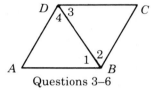

Questions 3–6

7. Find the value of $x$.

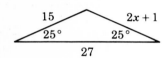

8. Find the value of $y$.

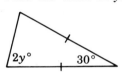

Using the given information, decide whether the two triangles must be congruent. If so, **(a)** write the congruence and **(b)** name the postulate or theorem that justifies your answer. If not, write *none* for both (a) and (b).

9. $\overline{BE} \perp \overline{AD}$; $\overline{AB} \cong \overline{DE}$;
   $C$ is the midpoint of $\overline{BE}$.

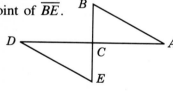

10. $\overline{FG} \cong \overline{HI}$;
    $\angle G \cong \angle I$

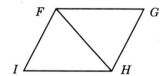

11. $\angle K$ and $\angle M$ are right angles;
    $\angle J \cong \angle N$; $\overline{JL} \cong \overline{NL}$

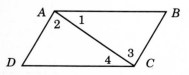

12. $\overrightarrow{PR}$ bisects $\angle QPS$;
    $\overline{PR} \perp \overline{QS}$

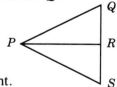

13. Write a two-column proof in the space at the right.

    Given: $\overline{AB} \parallel \overline{DC}$; $\angle B \cong \angle D$
    Prove: $\overline{AD} \cong \overline{BC}$

## Answers

1. a. _____ (3)

   b. _____ (3)

2. a. _____ (3)

   b. _____ (3)

   c. _____ (3)

   d. _____ (3)

3. _____ (5)

4. _____ (5)

5. _____ (5)

6. _____ (5)

7. _____ (6)

8. _____ (6)

9. a. _____ (5)

   b. _____ (4)

10. a _____ (5)

    b. _____ (4)

11. a _____ (5)

    b. _____ (4)

12. a _____ (5)

    b. _____ (4)

13. (See proof) _____ (14)

TESTS for GEOMETRY

## Test 16   *More about Proof in Geometry*

**Directions:** Write answers in the spaces provided.

In each diagram, identify $\overline{AB}$ as a *perpendicular bisector*, a *median*, an *altitude*, or a *bisector of an angle*.

**1.**

**2.**

**3.**

**4.**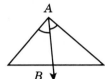

**5.**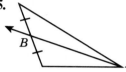

**6.**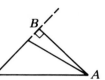

**7.** If $\overleftrightarrow{CD}$ is the perpendicular bisector of $\overline{AB}$, then $C$ is equidistant from __?__ and __?__ .

**8.** If $\overrightarrow{CD}$ bisects $\angle ACB$, then __?__ = __?__ .

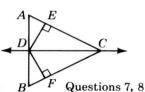

Questions 7, 8

In Question 9 the diagram is marked with the given information. Give the reason for each key step of the proof.

**9.** Prove: $\overline{BF} \cong \overline{DF}$

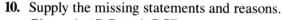

Key steps of proof:
**a.** $\triangle ABC \cong \triangle ADC$
**b.** $\angle 1 \cong \angle 2$
**c.** $\triangle BCF \cong \triangle DCF$
**d.** $\overline{BF} \cong \overline{DF}$

**Answers**

1. _____ (6)

2. _____ (6)

3. _____ (6)

4. _____ (6)

5. _____ (6)

6. _____ (6)

7. _____ (6)

8. _____ (6)

9. a. _____ (6)

   b. _____ (6)

   c. _____ (6)

   d. _____ (6)

10. (See proof) _____ (28)

**10.** Supply the missing statements and reasons.
Given: $\angle ADC \cong \angle BCD$;
$\overline{AD} \cong \overline{BC}$
Prove: $\angle DAB \cong \angle CBA$

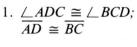

Proof:

| Statements | Reasons |
|---|---|
| 1. $\angle ADC \cong \angle BCD$; $\overline{AD} \cong \overline{BC}$ | 1. _____ |
| 2. _____ | 2. Reflexive Prop. |
| 3. $\triangle ADC \cong$ _____ | 3. _____ |
| 4. $\overline{DB} \cong \overline{CA}$ | 4. _____ |
| 5. $\overline{AB} \cong \overline{AB}$ | 5. _____ |
| 6. _____ | 6. _____ |
| 7. $\angle DAB \cong \angle CBA$ | 7. _____ |

# Test 17  *Chapter 4 Test*

**Directions:** Write answers in the spaces provided.

Complete each statement.

1. $\triangle ABC \cong$ ___?___

2. $\angle ACB \cong$ ___?___

3. $\overline{BA} \cong$ ___?___

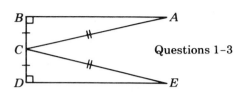

Questions 1–3

4. $\triangle PQR \cong$ ___?___

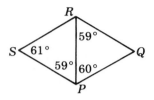

Question 4

Using the given information, decide whether the two triangles must be congruent. If so, **(a)** write the congruence and **(b)** name the postulate or theorem that justifies your answer. If not, write *none* for both (a) and (b).

5. $\overline{WY} \cong \overline{XY}$; $\overline{WZ} \cong \overline{XZ}$

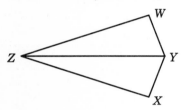

6. $\angle W$ and $\angle X$ are right angles; $\overline{WY} \cong \overline{XY}$

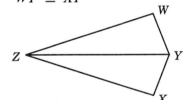

7. $X$ is the midpoint of $\overline{BC}$; $\overline{AB} \cong \overline{DC}$

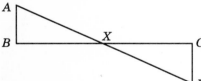

8. $\overline{AD}$ bisects $\overline{BC}$; $\overline{BC}$ bisects $\overline{AD}$.

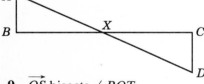

9. $\overrightarrow{QS}$ bisects $\angle RQT$; $\overline{QS} \perp \overline{RT}$

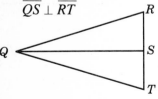

10. $\overrightarrow{YZ}$ bisects $\angle WYX$; $\overrightarrow{ZY}$ bisects $\angle WZX$.

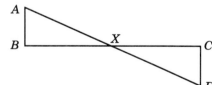

11. $\overline{PQ} \cong \overline{RS}$; $\overline{QT} \cong \overline{ST}$

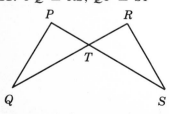

12. $\angle P$ and $\angle R$ are right angles; $\overline{QT} \cong \overline{ST}$

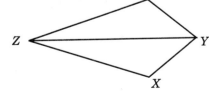

**Answers**

1. _____ (2)

2. _____ (2)

3. _____ (2)

4. _____ (3)

5. a. _____ (2)

   b. _____ (2)

6. a. _____ (2)

   b. _____ (2)

7. a. _____ (2)

   b. _____ (2)

8. a. _____ (2)

   b. _____ (2)

9. a. _____ (2)

   b. _____ (2)

10. a. _____ (2)

    b. _____ (2)

11. a. _____ (2)

    b. _____ (2)

12. a. _____ (2)

    b. _____ (2)

*(continued)*

## Test 17 (continued)

Given: $\overline{CD} \perp \overline{AB}$; $\overline{AF} \cong \overline{BF}$; $\angle ACE \cong \angle BCE$

**13.** Name an altitude of $\triangle ABC$.

**14.** Name a median of $\triangle ABC$.

**15.** Name an angle bisector.

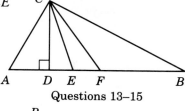

Questions 13–15

**16.** If $\angle BCD \cong \angle BDC$, name two segments that must be congruent.

**17.** If $\overline{AC} \cong \overline{AB}$, name two angles that must be congruent.

**18.** If $m\angle DAB = 20$ and $m\angle DBA = 20$, name two segments that must be congruent.

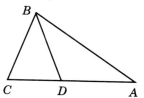

Questions 16–18

**19.** If $\overline{RS} \cong \overline{RP}$ and $m\angle 1 = 40$, then $m\angle 6 = \underline{\ ?\ }$.

**20.** If $\overline{RT} \cong \overline{RQ}$ and $m\angle 7 = 50$, then $m\angle 4 = \underline{\ ?\ }$.

**21.** If $\overline{RT} \cong \overline{RQ}$ and $m\angle 2 = 100$, then $m\angle 7 = \underline{\ ?\ }$.

**22.** If $\angle 1 \cong \angle 6$, $RS = 2x + 6$, $RT = 2x + 4$, $RQ = 3x - 2$, and $RP = 3x - 1$, then $x = \underline{\ ?\ }$.

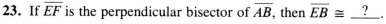

Questions 19–22

**23.** If $\overline{EF}$ is the perpendicular bisector of $\overline{AB}$, then $\overline{EB} \cong \underline{\ ?\ }$.

**24.** If $\overrightarrow{CE}$ bisects $\angle DCB$, then $\overline{EB} \cong \underline{\ ?\ }$.

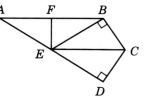

Questions 23, 24

**25.** Supply the missing statements and reasons.

Given: $\angle 1 \cong \angle 2$; $\angle 5 \cong \angle 6$
Prove: $\overrightarrow{EC}$ bisects $\angle BED$.

Proof:

| Statements | Reasons |
|---|---|
| 1. $\angle 1 \cong \angle 2$; $\angle 5 \cong \angle 6$ | 1. _____ |
| 2. _____ | 2. _____ |
| 3. $\triangle ACB \cong$ _____ | 3. _____ |
| 4. $\overline{BC} \cong \overline{DC}$ | 4. _____ |
| 5. $\overline{CE} \cong \overline{CE}$ | 5. _____ |
| 6. _____ | 6. _____ |
| 7. $\angle 3 \cong \angle 4$ | 7. _____ |
| 8. $\overrightarrow{EC}$ bisects $\angle BED$. | 8. _____ |

**Answers**

13. _____ (2)

14. _____ (2)

15. _____ (2)

16. _____ (3)

17. _____ (3)

18. _____ (3)

19. _____ (3)

20. _____ (3)

21. _____ (3)

22. _____ (3)

23. _____ (3)

24. _____ (3)

25. (See proof) _____ (8)

(continued)

## Test 17 (continued)

Write proofs in two-column form.

**26.** Given: $\overline{AB} \parallel \overline{CD}$; $\overline{EC} \cong \overline{ED}$

Prove: $\angle 1 \cong \angle 2$

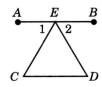

**27.** Given: $\angle RTV \cong \angle STV$;

$\overline{TV} \perp \overline{RS}$

Prove: $\overline{RT} \cong \overline{ST}$

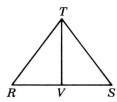

---

**CHALLENGE (Optional)**

How many pairs of triangles shown can be proved congruent?

**ANSWER**

_____

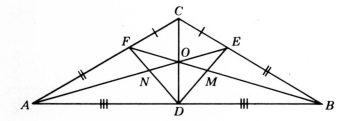

# Test 18   *Parallelograms*

**Directions:** Write answers in the spaces provided.

Quad. *KLMN* is a parallelogram. Complete each statement.

1. $\overline{KN} \cong$ _?_

2. $\angle NML \cong$ _?_

3. $\overline{MX} \cong$ _?_

4. $\angle 1 \cong$ _?_

5. $\angle KNM$ is supplementary to _?_ .

6. $\triangle MLN \cong$ _?_

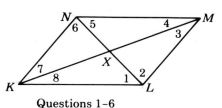

Questions 1–6

If it is possible to prove that a quadrilateral is a parallelogram from the given information, name the parallelogram. If it is not possible, write *none*.

7. $\overline{FA} \cong \overline{EB}; \overline{FA} \parallel \overline{EB}$

8. $\overline{FD} \cong \overline{AC}; \overline{AF} \cong \overline{CD}$

9. $\overline{FA} \parallel \overline{EB}; \overline{DC} \parallel \overline{EB}$

10. $\angle 1 \cong \angle 3; \angle 2 \cong \angle 4$

11. $\overline{FD} \parallel \overline{AC}; \overline{EB} \parallel \overline{DC}$

12. $\overline{FG} \cong \overline{GB}; \overline{AG} \cong \overline{GE}$

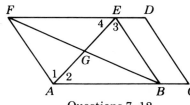

Questions 7–12

In Questions 13–20, complete each statement with the number that makes the statement true. If insufficient information is given to determine an answer, write *not possible*.

13. $DE =$ _?_

14. $m \angle B =$ _?_

15. $m \angle DFC =$ _?_

16. $AC =$ _?_

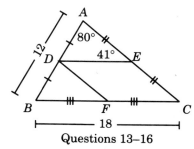

Questions 13–16

17. If $PQ = 5$, then $WX =$ _?_ .

18. If $YZ = 7$, then $XY =$ _?_ .

19. If $QX = 12$, then $PW =$ _?_ .

20. If $WZ = 20$, then $WX =$ _?_ .

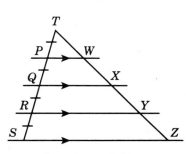

Questions 17–20

# Test 19    *Special Quadrilaterals*

**Directions:** Write answers in the spaces provided.

Quad. *HIJK* is a rhombus. Classify each statement as *must be true* or *not necessarily true.*

1. $\angle HIJ \cong \angle JKH$

2. $\angle IHJ \cong \angle KHJ$

3. $\overline{IK} \cong \overline{HJ}$

4. $\overline{IM} \cong \overline{KM}$

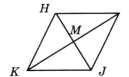
Questions 1–4

Quad. *RSTV* is a rectangle. Classify each statement as *must be true* or *not necessarily true.*

5. $\overline{RT} \cong \overline{VS}$

6. $\overline{RT} \perp \overline{VS}$

7. $\overrightarrow{TR}$ bisects $\angle VTS$.

8. $\overline{RX} \cong \overline{TX}$

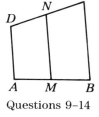
Questions 5–8

$\overline{MN}$ is the median of trapezoid *ABCD.*

9. If *DN* = 5, then *CD* = __?__ .

10. If $m \angle D$ = 100, then $m \angle DNM$ = __?__ .

11. If *AD* = 12 and *BC* = 20, then *MN* = __?__ .

12. If *MN* = $7\frac{1}{2}$ and *BC* = 9, then *AD* = __?__ .

13. If trapezoid *ABCD* is isosceles and $m \angle D$ = 100, then $m \angle A$ = __?__ .

14. If trapezoid *ABCD* is isosceles and *DN* = *x*, then *AB* = __?__ .

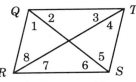
Questions 9–14

Using the given information, tell whether $\square QRST$ is best described as a *rectangle, rhombus,* or *square.*

15. $\overline{QS} \cong \overline{RT}$

16. $\overline{QS} \cong \overline{RT}; \overline{QS} \perp \overline{RT}$

17. $\overline{QR} \perp \overline{RS}$

18. $\angle 1 \cong \angle 2; \angle 3 \cong \angle 4$

Questions 15–18

19. In $\triangle ABC$ at the right, *MC* = __?__

20. $m \angle ACM$ = __?__

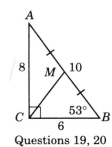
Questions 19, 20

**Answers**

1. _____ (5)

2. _____ (5)

3. _____ (5)

4. _____ (5)

5. _____ (5)

6. _____ (5)

7. _____ (5)

8. _____ (5)

9. _____ (5)

10. _____ (5)

11. _____ (5)

12. _____ (5)

13. _____ (5)

14. _____ (5)

15. _____ (5)

16. _____ (5)

17. _____ (5)

18. _____ (5)

19. _____ (5)

20. _____ (5)

TESTS for GEOMETRY

# Test 20  *Chapter 5 Test*

**Directions:** Write answers in the spaces provided.

Write the letter of *every* special quadrilateral that has the given property.
**(A)** parallelogram     **(C)** rhombus      **(E)** trapezoid
**(B)** rectangle         **(D)** square        **(F)** isosceles trapezoid

1. All angles are right angles.     2. All sides are congruent.

3. Diagonals are congruent.      4. Diagonals bisect each other.

5. Diagonals are perpendicular.    6. The quadrilateral is regular.

7. Both pairs of opposite sides are parallel.

8. Exactly one pair of opposite sides are parallel.

9. Both pairs of opposite sides are congruent.

10. Each diagonal bisects two angles.

Quad. *DKRT* is a parallelogram.

11. If $DK = 12$ and $KR = 8$, then $TR = \underline{\ ?\ }$.

12. If $DR = 28$ and $KT = 18$, then $HR = \underline{\ ?\ }$.

13. If $\overline{DR} \perp \overline{TK}$, then $\square DKRT$ must be a
_____ .
$\underline{\qquad ?\qquad}$
   *(rectangle, rhombus, square)*

14. If $m\angle 1 = 30$ and $m\angle 8 = 40$, then $m\angle RTD = \underline{\ ?\ }$.

15. If $m\angle 2 = 45$ and $m\angle 3 = 55$, then $m\angle 6 = \underline{\ ?\ }$.

16. If $TH = 2x + 1$ and $KH = 4x$, then $x = \underline{\ ?\ }$.

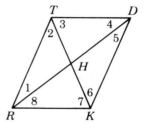

Questions 11–16

State whether the given information is sufficient to prove that quad. *MNOP* is a parallelogram. Write *yes* or *no*.

17. $\overline{MS} \cong \overline{OS}$; $\overline{NS} \cong \overline{PS}$

18. $\angle 1 \cong \angle 5$; $\angle 4 \cong \angle 8$

19. $\overline{PO} \cong \overline{MN}$; $\overline{PO} \parallel \overline{MN}$

20. $\angle PON \cong \angle PMN$; $\angle OPM \cong \angle ONM$

21. $\overline{MO} \cong \overline{NP}$; $\overline{MO} \perp \overline{NP}$

22. $\angle 1 \cong \angle 2$; $\angle 3 \cong \angle 4$

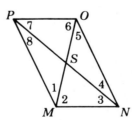

Questions 17–22

**Answers**

1. _____ (2)

2. _____ (2)

3. _____ (2)

4. _____ (2)

5. _____ (2)

6. _____ (2)

7. _____ (2)

8. _____ (2)

9. _____ (2)

10. _____ (2)

11. _____ (3)

12. _____ (3)

13. _____ (3)

14. _____ (3)

15. _____ (3)

16. _____ (3)

17. _____ (3)

18. _____ (3)

19. _____ (3)

20. _____ (3)

21. _____ (3)

22. _____ (3)

*(continued)*

## Test 20 (continued)

Given: $\overline{RW} \parallel \overline{SX} \parallel \overline{TY} \parallel \overline{VZ}$; $\overline{WX} \cong \overline{XY} \cong \overline{YZ}$.

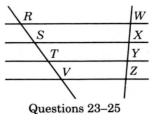

**23.** If $RS = 8$, then $TV = \underline{\ ?\ }$.

**24.** If $RV = 21$, then $RT = \underline{\ ?\ }$.

**25.** If $RT = 3x$ and $SV = x + 8$, find the value of $x$.

Questions 23–25

Given: $\angle ACB$ is a right angle; $D$, $E$, and $F$ are the midpoints of $\overline{AB}$, $\overline{BC}$, and $\overline{CA}$, respectively.

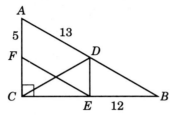

**26.** Find $CD$.

**27.** Find $EF$.

**28.** Find $ED$.

**29.** If $m \angle B = 23$, find $m \angle DCB$.

Questions 26–29

Given: $\overline{LM}$ is the median of trapezoid $HIJK$.

**30.** If $KJ = 7$ and $HI = 15$, find $LM$.

**31.** If $HI = 22$ and $LM = 17$, find $KJ$.

**32.** If trapezoid $HIJK$ is isosceles and $m \angle I = 85$, find $m \angle K$.

**33.** If $HI = 4x$, $LM = 2x + 3$, and $KJ = x - 2$, find the value of $x$.

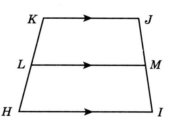

Questions 30–33

**34.** Write a two-column proof.

Given: $ABCD$ is an isosceles trapezoid with $\overline{AD} \parallel \overline{BC}$; $\overline{DE} \cong \overline{DC}$

Prove: $ABED$ is a parallelogram.

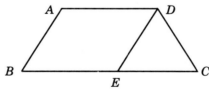

### Answers

23. _____ (3)

24. _____ (3)

25. _____ (3)

26. _____ (3)

27. _____ (3)

28. _____ (3)

29. _____ (3)

30. _____ (3)

31. _____ (3)

32. _____ (3)

33. _____ (4)

34. (See proof) _____ (10)

### CHALLENGE (Optional)

If $BE = x + 1$ and $DG = 5x - 9$, then $CF = \underline{\ ?\ }$.
*(numerical answer)*

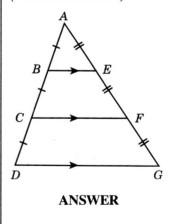

**ANSWER**

_____

# Test 21  *Cumulative Test, Chapters 4–5*

**Directions:** Write answers in the spaces provided.

Classify each statement as true or false.

**1.** If $\triangle ART \cong \triangle PIC$, then $\overline{AT} \cong \overline{PC}$.

**2.** If $\triangle ART \cong \triangle PIC$, then $\angle TAR \cong \angle CIP$.

**3.** The bisector of the vertex angle of an isosceles triangle is perpendicular to the base.

**4.** The diagonals of a quadrilateral bisect each other.

**5.** The length of the median from the vertex of the right angle of a right triangle equals half the length of the hypotenuse.

**6.** If the measure of the vertex angle of an isosceles triangle is 60, then the triangle is equilateral.

**7.** The diagonals of a rectangle are perpendicular.

**8.** If two sides and a non-included angle of one triangle are congruent to the corresponding parts of another triangle, then the triangles are congruent.

**9.** Any point on the perpendicular bisector of a segment is equidistant from the endpoints of the segment.

**10.** The measure of each acute angle of an isosceles right triangle is 45.

**Answers**

1. _____ (2)

2. _____ (2)

3. _____ (2)

4. _____ (2)

5. _____ (2)

6. _____ (2)

7. _____ (2)

8. _____ (2)

9. _____ (2)

10. _____ (2)

11. _____ (3)

12. _____ (3)

13. _____ (3)

14. _____ (3)

15. _____ (3)

16. _____ (3)

Using the given information, name the postulate or theorem that can be used to prove the triangles congruent. If the triangles cannot be proved congruent, write *none*.

**11.** $\overline{AB} \cong \overline{AD}$;
$\overline{BC} \cong \overline{DC}$

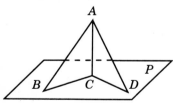

**12.** $\angle B \cong \angle D$;
$\overline{BC} \cong \overline{DC}$

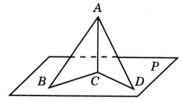

**13.** $\overline{AC} \perp$ plane $P$;
$\overline{AB} \cong \overline{AD}$

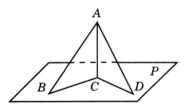

**14.** $\overline{GJ} \perp \overline{HI}$;
$\overrightarrow{GJ}$ bisects $\angle HGI$.

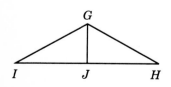

**15.** $J$ is the midpoint of $\overline{HI}$;
$\angle 1 \cong \angle 2$

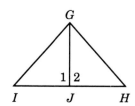

**16.** $\overline{MN} \cong \overline{SR}$;
$\angle N \cong \angle R$

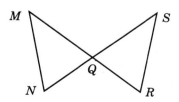

*(continued)*

## Test 21 (continued)

Determine whether each figure is best described as a *rectangle*, *rhombus*, or *square*.

**17.**

**18.**

**19.**

**20.**

Given $\overline{AB} \cong \overline{DC}$, $\angle A \cong \angle D$, and $\overline{AC} \cong \overline{DF}$, tell whether each statement must be true. Write *yes* or *no*.

**21.** $\angle 1 \cong \angle 4$

**22.** $\angle 2 \cong \angle 3$

**23.** $\angle DCF \cong \angle DCB$

**24.** $\overline{AC} \parallel \overline{DF}$

**25.** $C$ is the midpoint of $\overline{BF}$.

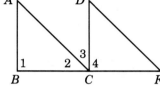

Questions 21–25

In Questions 26–29, $ABCD$ is a rhombus.

**26.** $m \angle CBX = \underline{\ ?\ }$

**27.** $m \angle AXB = \underline{\ ?\ }$

**28.** $DB = \underline{\ ?\ }$

**29.** $AB = \underline{\ ?\ }$

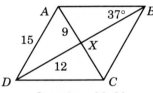

Questions 26–29

In Questions 30–34, $EFGH$ is an isosceles trapezoid with median $\overline{IJ}$.

**30.** $m \angle EFG = \underline{\ ?\ }$

**31.** $FG = \underline{\ ?\ }$

**32.** $IJ = \underline{\ ?\ }$

**33.** $IK = \underline{\ ?\ }$

**34.** $KG = \underline{\ ?\ }$

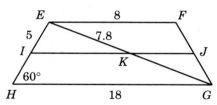

Questions 30–34

If it is possible to prove that a quadrilateral is a parallelogram from the given information, name the parallelogram. If it is not possible, write *none*.

**35.** $\angle 1 \cong \angle 11$; $\angle 12 \cong \angle 2$

**36.** $\angle 4 \cong \angle 8$; $\angle 5 \cong \angle 9$

**37.** $\overline{GC} \cong \overline{FD}$; $\overline{GF} \cong \overline{CD}$

**38.** $\overline{AC} \parallel \overline{HD}$; $\overline{HD} \parallel \overline{FE}$; $\overline{BC} \cong \overline{FE}$

**39.** $\overline{GT} \cong \overline{TE}$; $\overline{FT} \cong \overline{TD}$

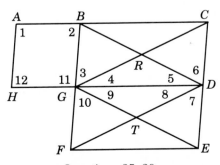

Questions 35–39

**Answers**

17. _____ (2)

18. _____ (2)

19. _____ (2)

20. _____ (2)

21. _____ (1)

22. _____ (1)

23. _____ (1)

24. _____ (1)

25. _____ (1)

26. _____ (2)

27. _____ (2)

28. _____ (2)

29. _____ (2)

30. _____ (2)

31. _____ (2)

32. _____ (2)

33. _____ (2)

34. _____ (2)

35. _____ (2)

36. _____ (2)

37. _____ (2)

38. _____ (2)

39. _____ (2)

*(continued)*

## Test 21 *(continued)*

Complete each statement.

**40.** If $\overline{BC} \cong \overline{AC}$, then $\angle B \cong$ __?__ .

**41.** If $\angle A \cong \angle C$, then $\overline{AB} \cong$ __?__ .

**42.** If $J$ is equidistant from $\overrightarrow{BA}$ and $\overrightarrow{BC}$, then $\overrightarrow{BJ}$ is a(n) __?__ of __?__ .

**43.** If $A$ and $X$ are both equidistant from $B$ and $C$, then $\overleftrightarrow{AX}$ is a(n) __?__ bisector of __?__ .

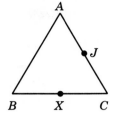

Questions 40–43

**40.** _____ (2)

**41.** _____ (2)

**42.** _____ (2)

**43.** _____ (2)

**44.** (See proof) _____ (5)

**45.** (See proof) _____ (8)

**44.** Supply the missing statements and reasons.

Given: $\overline{AB} \cong \overline{ED}$;
$\qquad \angle BAE \cong \angle DEA$
Prove: $\triangle ACE$ is isosceles.

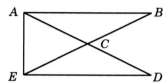

Proof:

| Statements | Reasons |
|---|---|
| 1. $\overline{AB} \cong \overline{ED}$; $\angle BAE \cong \angle DEA$ | 1. _____ |
| 2. $\overline{AE} \cong \overline{AE}$ | 2. _____ |
| 3. _____ | 3. _____ |
| 4. $\angle BEA \cong \angle DAE$ | 4. _____ |
| 5. $\overline{AC} \cong \overline{EC}$ | 5. _____ |
| 6. _____ | 6. _____ |

**45.** Write a two-column proof.

Given: $\overrightarrow{AN} \perp \overline{ST}$; $\overrightarrow{AN}$ bisects $\angle SAT$.
Prove: $N$ is the midpoint of $\overline{ST}$.

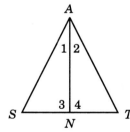

# Test 22  *Inequalities and Indirect Proof*  | Lessons 6-1 through 6-3 |

**Directions:** Write answers in the spaces provided.

Write the letter of the word that describes each form of the given conditional.

**(A)** Converse     **(B)** Inverse     **(C)** Contrapositive     **(D)** None of these

*If ice melts, then it is above freezing.*

  1.  If it is above freezing, then ice melts.

  2.  If ice does not melt, then it is not above freezing.

  3.  If ice does not melt, then it is above freezing.

  4.  If it is not above freezing, then ice does not melt.

What can you conclude by using the given statement together with each of the following statements? If no conclusion is possible, write *none*.

*Beebles have no teeth.*

  5.  Gork has no teeth.        **6.**  Blemp is not a beeble.

  7.  Felp is a beeble.         **8.**  Fang has teeth.

For each conditional, complete the following first sentence of an indirect proof: Assume temporarily that __?__ .

  9.  If $r + s = t$, then $r = t - s$.

  10.  If $a^3 > 0$, then $a > 0$.

  11.  If two lines are perpendicular, then they intersect.

Complete each statement by writing $<$, $=$, or $>$.

  12.  $AX$ __?__ $XC$

  13.  $m \angle ADC$ __?__ $m \angle 6$

  14.  $DX$ __?__ $DB$

  15.  $m \angle 4$ __?__ $m \angle 2$

  16.  $AD$ __?__ $BC$

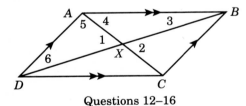

Questions 12–16

Complete each statement with the word *always*, *sometimes*, or *never*.

  17.  If a conditional is true, then its inverse is __?__ true.

  18.  The first step in an indirect proof is __?__ to assume temporarily that the hypothesis is not true.

  19.  The measure of an exterior angle of a triangle is __?__ greater than the measure of either remote interior angle.

  20.  The converse and inverse of a conditional are __?__ logically equivalent.

**Answers**

1. _____ (5)

2. _____ (5)

3. _____ (5)

4. _____ (5)

5. _____ (5)

   _____

6. _____ (5)

   _____

7. _____ (5)

   _____

8. _____ (5)

   _____

9. _____ (5)

10. _____ (5)

11. _____ (5)

   _____

12. _____ (5)

13. _____ (5)

14. _____ (5)

15. _____ (5)

16. _____ (5)

17. _____ (5)

18. _____ (5)

19. _____ (5)

20. _____ (5)

TESTS for GEOMETRY

# Test 23  *Inequalities in Triangles*

**Directions:** Write answers in the spaces provided.

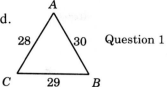

1. List the angles of the triangle in order from smallest to largest.

2. List the sides of the triangle in order from shortest to longest.

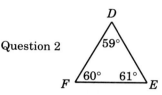

Question 2

Is it possible for a triangle to have sides with the lengths indicated?

**3.** 5, 9, 15          **4.** 1, 19, 18.5          **5.** 10, 7, 3

**6.** The lengths of two sides of a triangle are 15 and 26. The length of the third side must be greater than __?__ , but less than __?__ .

Complete each statement with *must be, may be,* or *cannot be.*

**7.** The altitude to the base of an isosceles triangle __?__ longer than the base.

**8.** The altitude to the base of an isosceles triangle __?__ longer than a leg of the triangle.

**9.** The sum of the lengths of the sides of an equilateral triangle __?__ longer than the sum of the lengths of the altitudes of the triangle.

In Questions 10–12, the diagrams are not drawn to scale. If each diagram were drawn to scale, which segment shown would be the shortest?

**10.** 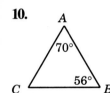          **11.** 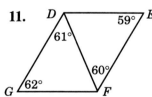          **12.**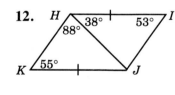

In Questions 13–15, the diagrams are not drawn to scale. If each diagram were drawn to scale, which numbered angle would be smaller, $\angle 1$ or $\angle 2$?

**13.**           **14.** 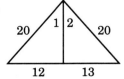          **15.**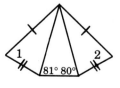

**16.** If $AB > AD$, then $m \angle$ __?__ $> m \angle$ __?__ .          **17.** $AC + CB >$ __?__

**18.** If $m \angle B > m \angle 1$, then __?__ > __?__ .

**19.** If $AD = AC = CB$, then which segment is shorter, $\overline{DC}$ or $\overline{AB}$?

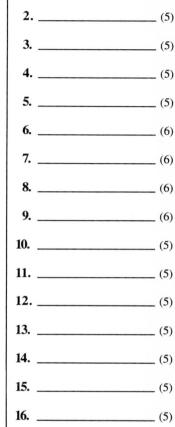

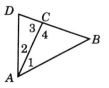

Questions 16–19

**Answers**

1. _____ (5)

2. _____ (5)

3. _____ (5)

4. _____ (5)

5. _____ (5)

6. _____ (6)

7. _____ (6)

8. _____ (6)

9. _____ (6)

10. _____ (5)

11. _____ (5)

12. _____ (5)

13. _____ (5)

14. _____ (5)

15. _____ (5)

16. _____ (5)

17. _____ (5)

18. _____ (5)

19. _____ (6)

# Test 24    *Chapter 6 Test*

**Directions:** Write answers in the spaces provided.

For Questions 1–6, identify each statement as the *converse, inverse,* or *contrapositive* of the given conditional.

> *If the weather is clear, then the launch will be held.*

1. If the weather is not clear, then the launch will not be held.

2. If the launch will be held, then the weather is clear.

3. If the launch will not be held, then the weather is not clear.

> *If a triangle is equilateral, then it is isosceles.*

4. If a triangle is not isosceles, then it is not equilateral.

5. If a triangle is isosceles, then it is equilateral.

6. If a triangle is not equilateral, then it is not isosceles.

Accept the given statement as true. What can you conclude by using the given statement together with each additional statement? If no conclusion is possible, write *no conclusion.*

> *If the Crawdads play, then the party will be a success.*

7. The Crawdads did not play.

8. The party was a success.

9. The party was a failure.

10. The Crawdads played.

Draw a Venn diagram to represent each statement below.

11. If a car is new, then it has seat belts.

12. Every square is a quadrilateral.

**Answers**

1. _____ (3)

2. _____ (3)

3. _____ (3)

4. _____ (3)

5. _____ (3)

6. _____ (3)

7. _____ (3)

_____

8. _____ (3)

_____

9. _____ (3)

_____

10. _____ (3)

_____

11. (See question) _____ (3)

12. (See question) _____ (3)

13. _____ (4)

14. _____ (3)

15. _____ (3)

---

13. Write the letters **(A)**–**(D)** in an order that completes the indirect proof of the statement: If $x - 3 = 7$, then $x \neq 5$.
    **(A)** But this contradicts the given fact that $x - 3 = 7$.
    **(B)** Then $x - 3 = 2$.
    **(C)** Thus the temporary assumption is false and $x \neq 5$.
    **(D)** Assume temporarily that $x = 5$.

14. List the angles of $\triangle ABC$ in order from largest to smallest.

15. List the sides of $\triangle DEF$ in order from longest to shortest.

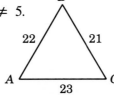

Question 14

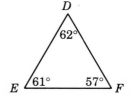

Question 15

*(continued)*

## Test 24 *(continued)*

In Questions 16–20, classify each statement as true or false.

**16.** In an isosceles triangle, if the base is longer than either leg, then the measure of each base angle is greater than the measure of the vertex angle.

**17.** The sum of the lengths of two sides of a triangle is greater than the length of the third side.

**18.** The shortest segment from a point to a line is the perpendicular segment from the point to the line.

**19.** The sum of the lengths of the diagonals of a rhombus is less than its perimeter.

**20.** If two isosceles triangles have congruent legs but noncongruent bases, then the triangle with the longer base has the smaller base angles.

**21.** The lengths of two sides of a triangle are 4 and 9. The length of the third side must be greater than __?__ , but less than __?__ .

**22.** Is is possible for a triangle to have sides with the lengths indicated?
  **a.** 10, 5, 4      **b.** 9, 6, 8

**23.** Which segment is longer?
  **a.** $\overline{AB}$ or $\overline{BC}$
  **b.** $\overline{AB}$ or $\overline{AD}$

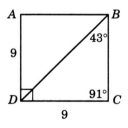

**24.** Which angle is larger?
  **a.** $\angle JKM$ or $\angle LKM$
  **b.** $\angle MLK$ or $\angle MKL$

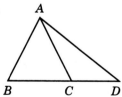

**25.** Write a two-column proof.
  Given: $\overline{AB} \cong \overline{AC}$
  Prove: $m\angle B > m\angle D$

### Answers

16. _____ (3)

17. _____ (3)

18. _____ (3)

19. _____ (3)

20. _____ (3)

21. _____ (3)

22. a. _____ (3)

  b. _____ (3)

23. a. _____ (4)

  b. _____ (4)

24. a. _____ (4)

  b. _____ (4)

25. (See proof) _____ (14)

---

**Challenge (Optional)**

Find the shortest segment in the figure.

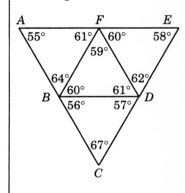

**ANSWER**

_____

TESTS for GEOMETRY
**SHEET 35**

# Test 25   *Ratio, Proportion, and Similarity*   | Lessons 7-1 through 7-3 |

**Directions:** Write answers in the spaces provided.

Express each ratio in simplest form.

**1.** $\frac{14}{18}$

**2.** $\frac{11x^2}{6xy}$

**3.** 8 inches to 2 feet

Use the diagram to express each ratio in simplest form.

**4.** $AB : BD$

**5.** $AD : AC$

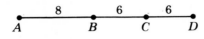

Questions 4, 5

**6.** The ratio of the measures of two complementary angles is 2:3. Find the measure of each angle.

Find the value of $x$.

**7.** $\frac{x}{9} = \frac{4}{3}$

**8.** $\frac{5}{6} = \frac{x+2}{9}$

**9.** $\frac{1}{x-3} = \frac{3}{x+1}$

**10.** If $\frac{x}{5} = \frac{6}{y} = \frac{8}{20}$, find the values of **(a)** $x$ and **(b)** $y$.

In the diagram at the right, $\frac{AD}{DC} = \frac{BE}{EC}$.

**11.** If $AD = 9$, $DC = 6$, and $BE = 12$, find $EC$.

**12.** If $AC = 27$, $BE = 25$, and $EC = 20$, find $AD$.

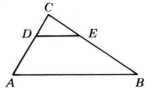

Questions 11, 12

**13.** The second and third terms of a proportion are called the __?__ .

**14.** If $\frac{a}{b} = \frac{4}{7}$, then $\frac{a+b}{b} = \frac{?}{7}$.

In Questions 15–19, quad. *ABCD* ~ quad. *RSTV*.

**15.** What is the scale factor of quad. *ABCD* to quad. *RSTV*?

**16.** Find $m \angle B$.

**17.** Find $m \angle T$.

**18.** Find *RS*.

**19.** Find *BC*.

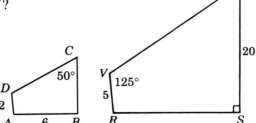

Questions 15–19

**Answers**

1. _____ (5)

2. _____ (5)

3. _____ (5)

4. _____ (5)

5. _____ (5)

6. _____ (5)

7. _____ (5)

8. _____ (5)

9. _____ (5)

10. a. _____ (5)

    b. _____ (5)

11. _____ (5)

12. _____ (5)

13. _____ (5)

14. _____ (5)

15. _____ (5)

16. _____ (5)

17. _____ (5)

18. _____ (5)

19. _____ (5)

# Test 26  *Supplementary Test*

**Directions:** Write answers in the spaces provided.

In Questions 1–3, $\triangle COG \sim \triangle BAT$.

**1.** $\angle C \cong$ __?__

**2.** $\dfrac{CG}{BT} = \dfrac{OG}{?}$

**3.** $\triangle OCG \sim$ __?__

$ABCD$ is an isosceles trapezoid with $\overline{BC} \parallel \overline{AD}$. Find the value of each ratio.

**4.** $BC : AD$

**5.** $m \angle A : m \angle D$

**6.** $AD :$ perimeter of $ABCD$

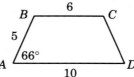

Questions 4–6

**7.** Quad. I $\sim$ quad. II. Complete.
   **a.** The scale factor of quad. I to quad. II is __?__ .
   **b.** Quad. $ABCD \sim$ quad. __?__
   **c.** $x =$ __?__   **d.** $y =$ __?__

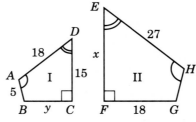

**8.** List the three reasons that can be used to prove that two triangles are similar.

Can the two triangles shown be proved similar? If so, state the similarity and tell which similarity postulate or theorem you would use. If not, write *none*.

**9.**

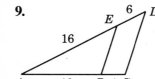

**10.**

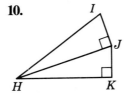

**11.**

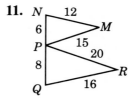

**12.**

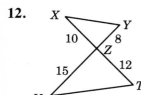

**13.**

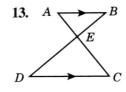

**14.**

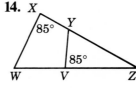

**15.** A man 6 ft tall casts a 21 ft shadow at the same time a tree casts a 70 ft shadow. How tall is the tree?

Complete.

**16.** $CD =$ __?__

**17.** $ED =$ __?__

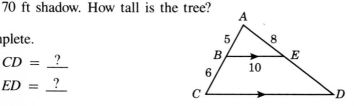

**Answers**

1. _____ (4)

2. _____ (4)

3. _____ (4)

4. _____ (5)

5. _____ (5)

6. _____ (5)

7. a. _____ (4)

b. _____ (4)

c. _____ (4)

d. _____ (4)

8. _____ (12)

_____

9. _____ (5)

10. _____ (5)

11. _____ (5)

12. _____ (5)

13. _____ (5)

14. _____ (5)

15. _____ (5)

16. _____ (5)

17. _____ (5)

# Test 27  *Working with Similar Triangles*

**Lessons 7-4 through 7-6**

**Directions:** Write answers in the spaces provided.

Tell whether the triangles are similar or not similar.

**1.**

**2.**
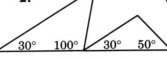

30° 100° 30° 50°

**3.** 75°
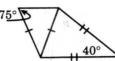
40°

**4.**
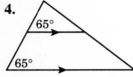
65°
65°

**5.**
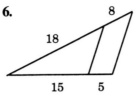
60°
20°
100°

**6.**
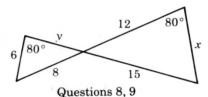
8
18
15  5

**7.** If $\triangle MNP \sim \triangle QSV$, complete the proportion: $\dfrac{MN}{?} = \dfrac{MP}{?} = \dfrac{NP}{?}$.

**8.** Find the value of $x$.

**9.** Find the value of $y$.

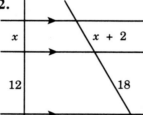
12  80°
y
6  80°
8  15  x

Questions 8, 9

Find the value of $x$.

**10.**
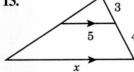
16
12
20  $x$

**11.**
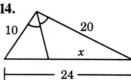
9
15  $x$
25

**12.**
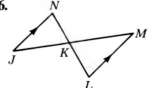
$x$  $x + 2$
12  18

**13.**
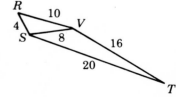
3
5  4
$x$

**14.**
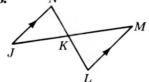
10  20
$x$
|— 24 —|

**Answers**

1. _____ (5)

2. _____ (5)

3. _____ (5)

4. _____ (5)

5. _____ (5)

6. _____ (5)

7. _____ (5)

8. _____ (5)

9. _____ (5)

10. _____ (5)

11. _____ (5)

12. _____ (5)

13. _____ (5)

14. _____ (5)

15. a. _____ (5)

    b. _____ (5)

16. a. _____ (5)

    b. _____ (5)

17. a. _____ (5)

    b. _____ (5)

Decide whether the two triangles must be similar. If so, **(a)** write the similarity and **(b)** name the postulate or theorem that justifies your answer. If not, write *none* for both (a) and (b).

**15.**
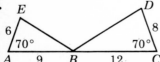
E  D
6  8
70°  70°
A  9  B  12  C

**16.**
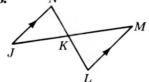
N
M
J  K
L

**17.**
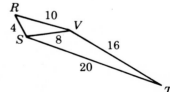
R  10
4  V
S  8  16
20
T

# Test 28   *Chapter 7 Test*

**Directions:** Write answers in the spaces provided.

Find the value of $x$.

**1.** $\dfrac{10}{x} = \dfrac{25}{15}$

**2.** $\dfrac{2x}{7} = \dfrac{x-1}{3}$

Complete each statement.

**3.** If $\dfrac{a}{b} = \dfrac{9}{4}$, then $4a = \underline{\ ?\ }$ .

**4.** If $\dfrac{x}{3} = \dfrac{8}{y}$, then $\dfrac{y}{3} = \underline{\ ?\ }$ .

**5.** If $\dfrac{x}{7} = \dfrac{5}{3}$, then $\dfrac{x+7}{7} = \underline{\ ?\ }$ .

**6.** If $3r = 4s$, then $\dfrac{r}{s} = \underline{\ ?\ }$ .

In Questions 7–9, $\triangle ABC \sim \triangle DEC$.

**7.** What is the scale factor of $\triangle ABC$ to $\triangle DEC$?

**8.** Find $AC$.

**9.** Find $DE$.

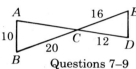

Questions 7–9

Tell whether the triangles are similar or not similar.

**10.**

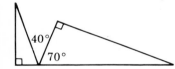

**11.**

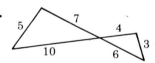

**12.**

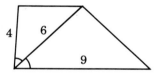

**13.**

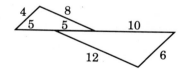

In Questions 14–17, quad. *MNTS* ~ quad. *MOPR*.

**14.** What is the scale factor of quad. *MNTS* to quad. *MOPR*?

**15.** Find *OP*.

**16.** Find *ST*.

**17.** Find *RS*.

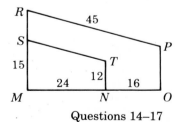

Questions 14–17

**18.** Find *DF*.

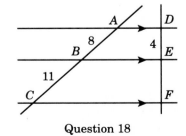

Question 18

**Answers**

1. _____ (4)

2. _____ (4)

3. _____ (4)

4. _____ (4)

5. _____ (4)

6. _____ (4)

7. _____ (4)

8. _____ (4)

9. _____ (4)

10. _____ (4)

11. _____ (4)

12. _____ (4)

13. _____ (4)

14. _____ (4)

15. _____ (4)

16. _____ (4)

17. _____ (4)

18. _____ (4)

*(continued)*

## Test 28 *(continued)*

**19.** If $\overrightarrow{GH}$ bisects $\angle EGF$, find *HF*.

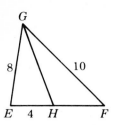

**20.** If $\overline{DE} \parallel \overline{AB}$, $AD = 5$, $DC = 8$, and $BE = 4$, find *EC*.

**21.** If $\overline{EF} \parallel \overline{CA}$, $BE = 4$, $BF = 10$, $EC = x - 1$, and $AF = 2x + 1$, find the value of *x*.

**22.** If $\overline{DE} \parallel \overline{AB}$, $CD = 10$, $DE = 8$, and $AD = 6$, find *AB*.

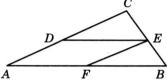

Questions 20–22

**23.** A tower casts a shadow 48 m long. Tom is 2 m tall and casts a shadow 8 m long while standing beside the tower. How tall is the tower?

**24.** Write a two-column proof.

Given: $\overline{AB} \parallel \overline{DC}$;
$\overline{BC} \parallel \overline{AE}$

Prove: $\dfrac{BC}{EA} = \dfrac{BD}{EB}$

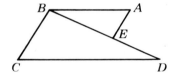

**Answers**

19. _____ (4)

20. _____ (4)

21. _____ (4)

22. _____ (4)

23. _____ (4)

24. (See proof) _____ (8)

**CHALLENGE (Optional)**
Angles are congruent as marked. Find the value of *x*.

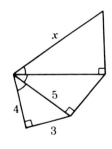

**ANSWER**

## Test 29    *Cumulative Test, Chapters 6–7*

**Directions:** Write answers in the spaces provided.

Write the letter of the word that describes each form of the given conditional.

**(A)** Converse      **(B)** Inverse      **(C)** Contrapositive      **(D)** None of these

*If it's an ostrich, then it doesn't fly.*

**1.** If it's not an ostrich, it flies.

**2.** If it doesn't fly, it's an ostrich.

**3.** If it flies, it's an ostrich.

**4.** If it flies, it's not an ostrich.

Accept the given conditional as true. What can you conclude by using the given statement together with each additional statement? If no conclusion is possible, write *no conclusion.*

*If it's a bird, then it has wings.*

**5.** The European pipistrelle isn't a bird.

**6.** The Baltimore oriole is a bird.

**7.** Polly doesn't have wings.

Complete the first sentence of an indirect proof of each conditional: Assume temporarily that 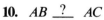 .

**8.** If $x = 7$, then $x + 3 \neq 11$.

**9.** If *ABCD* is a rhombus, then $\overline{AC} \perp \overline{BD}$.

Complete each statement by writing $<$, $=$, or $>$. If no conclusion is possible, write *no conclusion.*

**10.** $AB \underline{\ ?\ } AC$

**11.** $m\angle 1 + m\angle 2 \underline{\ ?\ } m\angle EAB$

**12.** $AB \underline{\ ?\ } BC$

**13.** $m\angle 5 \underline{\ ?\ } m\angle 3$

**14.** $m\angle 5 \underline{\ ?\ } m\angle 4$

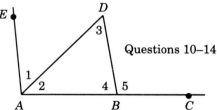

Questions 10–14

Complete.

**15.** In $\triangle ABC$, the largest angle is $\underline{\ ?\ }$ .

**16.** In $\triangle ABC$, the smallest angle is $\underline{\ ?\ }$ .

**17.** In $\triangle LMN$, the longest side is $\underline{\ ?\ }$ .

**18.** In $\triangle LMN$, the shortest side is $\underline{\ ?\ }$ .

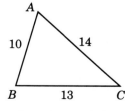

Questions 15, 16

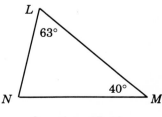

Questions 17, 18

**Answers**

1. _____ (2)

2. _____ (2)

3. _____ (2)

4. _____ (2)

5. _____ (2)

6. _____ (2)

7. _____ (2)

8. _____ (2)

9. _____ (2)

10. _____ (2)

11. _____ (2)

12. _____ (2)

13. _____ (2)

14. _____ (2)

15. _____ (2)

16. _____ (2)

17. _____ (2)

18. _____ (2)

*(continued)*

## Test 29 *(continued)*

In Questions 19–21, $\overline{BA} \cong \overline{BC}$, and $m \angle A = 55$.

19. If $AB = 10$, $BX = 8.2$, $AX = 6$, and $XC = 5.5$, then which angle is larger, $\angle 1$ or $\angle 2$?

20. If $m \angle 1 = 34$, then which segment is longer, $\overline{AX}$ or $\overline{XC}$?

21. Which segment is longer, $\overline{AB}$ or $\overline{AC}$?

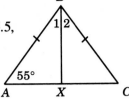

Questions 19–21

Complete.

22. If $\frac{3m}{5} = \frac{7}{2}$, then $m = \underline{\ ?\ }$.

23. If $\frac{a}{8} = \frac{5}{b}$, then $\frac{5}{a} = \frac{?}{?}$.

24. If $\frac{r}{8} = \frac{3}{11}$, then $\frac{r + 8}{8} = \frac{?}{?}$.

In Questions 25–29, quad. I ~ quad. II.

25. Complete:
Quad. $ABCG$ ~ quad. $\underline{\ ?\ }$.

26. Find the value of $x$.

27. Find the value of $y$.

28. Must $\overline{FC}$ be perpendicular to $\overline{BD}$?

Explain. _____

29. What is the scale factor of quad. I to quad. II?

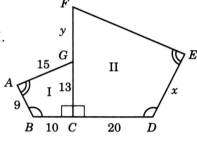

Questions 25–29

30. Find $TU$.    Questions 30, 31

31. Find $SU$.

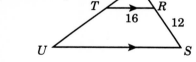

Decide whether the two triangles must be similar. If so, **(a)** write the similarity and **(b)** name the postulate or theorem that justifies your answer. If not, write *none* for both (a) and (b).

| Answers | |
|---|---|
| 19. _____ | (2) |
| 20. _____ | (2) |
| 21. _____ | (2) |
| 22. _____ | (2) |
| 23. _____ | (2) |
| 24. _____ | (2) |
| 25. _____ | (2) |
| 26. _____ | (2) |
| 27. _____ | (2) |
| 28. (See question) _____ | (2) |
| 29. _____ | (2) |
| 30. _____ | (3) |
| 31. _____ | (3) |
| 32. a. _____ | (2) |
| b. _____ | (1) |
| 33. a. _____ | (2) |
| b. _____ | (1) |
| 34. a. _____ | (2) |
| b. _____ | (1) |
| 35. a. _____ | (2) |
| b. _____ | (1) |

32.

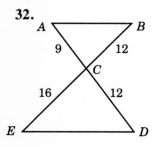

33.

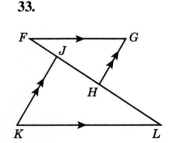

34.

35.

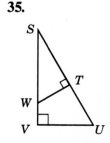

*(continued)*

## Test 29 *(continued)*

**36.** Find *WZ*.

**37.** Find *LM*.

**38.** Find *MP*.

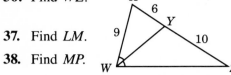

Question 36

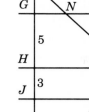

Questions 37, 38

**39.** Write a two-column proof.

Given: $\angle 1 \cong \angle 2$; $\overline{AB} \perp \overline{CD}$

Prove: $\dfrac{CB}{AB} = \dfrac{AC}{AD}$

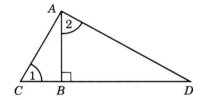

**40.** Write an indirect proof.

Given: $m\angle 1 = 50$; $m\angle 2 = 52$

Prove: $a \not\parallel b$

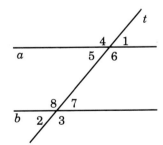

# Test 30  *Cumulative Test, Chapters 1–7*

**Directions:** Write answers in the spaces provided.

Indicate the best answer by writing the appropriate letter.

**Answers**

1. _____ (2)

2. _____ (2)

3. _____ (2)

4. _____ (2)

5. _____ (2)

6. _____ (2)

7. _____ (2)

8. _____ (2)

9. _____ (2)

10. _____ (2)

1. Which of the following set(s) of points are *not* collinear?
   (A) *A* and *B*   (B) *D, A,* and *H*
   (C) *D, B,* and *G*   (D) *G, C,* and *B*

2. $\overleftrightarrow{DH}$ and $\overleftrightarrow{GC}$ are called __?__ lines.
   (A) parallel   (B) intersecting
   (C) skew   (D) perpendicular

3. The intersection of plane *P* and plane *Q* is __?__ .
   (A) $\overleftrightarrow{KC}$   (B) $\overleftrightarrow{GB}$
   (C) $\overline{GC}$   (D) $\overline{GB}$

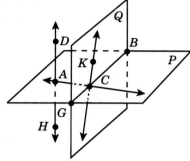

Questions 1–3

4. If *M* is between *R* and *T*, then __?__ .
   (A) *MR* + *RT* = *MT*   (B) *RM* = *MT*   (C) *RM* + *MT* = *RT*
   (D) *MR* = *RT*   (E) none of these

5. Which of the following is *not* a set of points?
   (A) $\overleftrightarrow{AB}$   (B) $\overrightarrow{AB}$   (C) $\overline{AB}$
   (D) *AB*   (E) none of these

6. If the measures of two supplementary angles are *x* + 10 and *x* − 20, then the measure of the smaller angle is __?__ .
   (A) 30   (B) 50   (C) 75
   (D) 95   (E) none of these

7. The two angles in a pair of vertical angles are always __?__ .
   (A) congruent   (B) adjacent   (C) acute
   (D) congruent and acute   (E) none of these

8. If two angles are complementary to the same angle, then they are __?__ to each other.
   (A) complementary   (B) vertical   (C) adjacent
   (D) congruent   (E) none of these

9. In a plane, two lines perpendicular to the same line are __?__ parallel.
   (A) always   (B) sometimes   (C) never

10. Two lines parallel to the same plane are __?__ parallel to each other.
    (A) always   (B) sometimes   (C) never

*(continued)*

## Test 30 *(continued)*

**11.** Which of the following is the hypothesis of the conditional:
I'll stay if I win.
  **(A)** I'll stay.      **(B)** I win.      **(C)** If I stay, I won.
  **(D)** I'll leave if I lose.  **(E)** I'll win if I stay.

**12.** Which of the following triangles does *not* exist?
  I. acute isosceles          II. right scalene
  III. obtuse equilateral        IV. obtuse scalene
  **(A)** I only        **(B)** II only        **(C)** III only
  **(D)** II and III      **(E)** II, III, and IV

**13.** Choose the statements that *must* be true for a rhombus.
  I. The diagonals are congruent.      II. The diagonals bisect each other.
  III. The diagonals are perpendicular.  IV. The diagonals bisect the angles.
  **(A)** I, II, and III    **(B)** II, III, and IV    **(C)** I, II, and IV
  **(D)** I, III, and IV    **(E)** all of these

**14.** Choose the statements that *must* be true for a rectangle.
  I. The diagonals are congruent.      II. The diagonals bisect each other.
  III. The diagonals are perpendicular.  IV. The diagonals bisect the angles.
  **(A)** I and II        **(B)** I and III        **(C)** I and IV
  **(D)** II and IV      **(E)** I, II, and IV

**15.** If $\triangle CAT \cong \triangle DOG$, then which of the following are true?
  I. $\angle A \cong \angle O$      II. $AT = DO$
  III. $TC = GD$        IV. $\triangle CTA \cong \triangle DGO$
  **(A)** I, II, and III    **(B)** I, II, and IV    **(C)** I, III, and IV
  **(D)** I and IV      **(E)** IV only

**16.** If two polygons are similar then which of the following *must* be true?
  I. The corresponding sides are in proportion.
  II. The perimeters are equal.
  III. The corresponding sides are congruent.
  IV. The corresponding angles are congruent.
  **(A)** I and II        **(B)** I and IV        **(C)** II and III
  **(D)** III and IV      **(E)** IV only

**17.** Which of the following methods can be used to prove a quadrilateral is a
parallelogram?
  I. Show that both pairs of opposite angles are congruent.
  II. Show that the diagonals are perpendicular.
  III. Show that both pairs of opposite sides are congruent.
  IV. Show that the diagonals bisect each other.
  **(A)** I, II, and IV    **(B)** I, III, and IV    **(C)** II, III, and IV
  **(D)** III and IV      **(E)** all of these

| | |
|---|---|
| **11.** _____ | (2) |
| **12.** _____ | (2) |
| **13.** _____ | (2) |
| **14.** _____ | (2) |
| **15.** _____ | (2) |
| **16.** _____ | (2) |
| **17.** _____ | (2) |

*(continued)*

TESTS for GEOMETRY
**SHEET 45**

## Test 30 *(continued)*

**Answers**

**18.** If $r \parallel s$, then $\angle 1$ is congruent to __?__.

    **(A)** $\angle 9$     **(B)** $\angle 11$

    **(C)** $\angle 5$     **(D)** $\angle 9$ and $\angle 5$

**19.** If $\angle 6$ is congruent to $\angle 10$, then __?__.

    **(A)** $b \parallel c$     **(B)** $r \parallel s$

    **(C)** $b \parallel c$ and $r \parallel s$     **(D)** none of these

**20.** If $\angle 3$ is congruent to $\angle 12$, then __?__.

    **(A)** $b \parallel c$     **(B)** $r \parallel s$

    **(C)** $b \parallel c$ and $r \parallel s$     **(D)** none of these

Questions 18–21

**21.** If $b \parallel c$, then $\angle 6$ must be __?__ to $\angle 3$.

    **(A)** congruent     **(B)** supplementary     **(C)** congruent and supplementary

    **(D)** adjacent     **(E)** congruent and adjacent

**22.** If two angles of a triangle measure 47 and 93, then the measure of the third angle is __?__.

    **(A)** 46     **(B)** 30     **(C)** 50

    **(D)** 60     **(E)** none of these

**23.** The sum of the measures of the exterior angles, one at each vertex, of a convex octagon is __?__.

    **(A)** 135     **(B)** 1080     **(C)** 45

    **(D)** 360     **(E)** none of these

**24.** Find the measure of each interior angle of a regular polygon with 10 sides.

    **(A)** 144     **(B)** 180     **(C)** 36

    **(D)** 135     **(E)** none of these

**25.** In parallelogram $ABCD$, $\triangle BCD$ is congruent to __?__.

    **(A)** $\triangle BAD$     **(B)** $\triangle DBA$     **(C)** $\triangle DAB$     **(D)** $\triangle ADB$

For Questions 26–29, which of the following postulates and theorems could be used to justify the conclusion?

**(A)** SSS     **(B)** SAS     **(C)** ASA     **(D)** AAS     **(E)** HL

**26.** If $\overline{AX} \perp \overline{BC}$ and $X$ is the midpoint of $\overline{BC}$, then $\triangle ABX \cong \triangle ACX$.

**27.** If $\overline{AX} \perp \overline{BC}$ and $\overrightarrow{AX}$ bisects $\angle BAC$, then $\triangle ABX \cong \triangle ACX$.

**28.** If $GH = GK$ and $HJ = KJ$, then $\triangle GHJ \cong \triangle GKJ$.

**29.** If $\overline{GH} \perp \overline{HJ}$, $\overline{GK} \perp \overline{KJ}$, and $GH = GK$, then $\triangle GHJ \cong \triangle GKJ$.

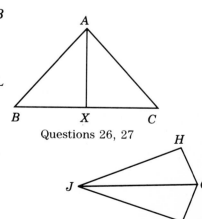

Questions 26, 27

Questions 28, 29

**18.** _____ (2)

**19.** _____ (2)

**20.** _____ (2)

**21.** _____ (2)

**22.** _____ (2)

**23.** _____ (2)

**24.** _____ (2)

**25.** _____ (2)

**26.** _____ (2)

**27.** _____ (2)

**28.** _____ (2)

**29.** _____ (2)

*(continued)*

## Test 30 *(continued)*

**Answers**

30. The diagonals of a trapezoid __?__ bisect each other.

    **(A)** always        **(B)** sometimes        **(C)** never

31. If the corresponding angles of two polygons are congruent, then the polygons are __?__ similar.

    **(A)** always        **(B)** sometimes        **(C)** never

32. If the lengths of the bases of a trapezoid are 19 and 33, then the length of the median is __?__ .

    **(A)** 52        **(B)** 14        **(C)** 26

    **(D)** 21        **(E)** none of these

33. If the lengths of two sides of a triangle are 7 and 13, then the length of the third side must be between __?__ and __?__ .

    **(A)** 8, 12        **(B)** 7, 19        **(C)** 7, 20

    **(D)** 6, 20        **(E)** none of these

34. In $\triangle ABC$, $m\angle A = 4x + 5$, $m\angle B = 2x + 20$, and $m\angle C = 5x - 10$. The congruent sides of the triangle are __?__ .

    **(A)** $\overline{AB}$ and $\overline{AC}$    **(B)** $\overline{AB}$ and $\overline{BC}$    **(C)** $\overline{AC}$ and $\overline{BC}$

    **(D)** $\overline{AB}$, $\overline{BC}$, and $\overline{AC}$    **(E)** none of these

35. If $ABCD$ is a parallelogram, then which of the following must be true?

    **(A)** $\angle A \cong \angle D$        **(B)** $\overline{AB} \cong \overline{DA}$        **(C)** $\overline{AB} \cong \overline{BC}$

    **(D)** $m\angle B + m\angle C = 180$

36. In $\triangle QRS$, $QR = 6$, $RS = 7$, and $QS = 8$. The largest angle of the triangle is __?__ .

    **(A)** $\angle Q$        **(B)** $\angle R$        **(C)** $\angle S$        **(D)** Answer cannot be determined.

37. The ratio of the measures of two complementary angles is $4 : 11$. The measure of the larger angle is __?__ .

    **(A)** 48        **(B)** 66        **(C)** 24        **(D)** 132        **(E)** none of these

38. Which of the following is the contrapositive of the statement: If the lake is frozen, then it is cold?

    **(A)** If it is cold, then the lake is frozen.

    **(B)** If it isn't cold, then the lake isn't frozen.

    **(C)** If the lake isn't frozen, then it isn't cold.

    **(D)** none of these

39. If $r : s = 3 : 7$, then $r : 3 = $ __?__ .

    **(A)** $s : 7$    **(B)** $7 : s$    **(C)** $r : 7$    **(D)** $s : 3$    **(E)** $7 : 3$

**Answers**

30. _____ (2)

31. _____ (2)

32. _____ (2)

33. _____ (2)

34. _____ (2)

35. _____ (2)

36. _____ (2)

37. _____ (2)

38. _____ (2)

39. _____ (2)

*(continued)*

## Test 30 *(continued)*

For Questions 40–43, decide which conclusion is possible.

**(A)** $\triangle ABC \sim \triangle DEC$ by AA Similarity Postulate
**(B)** $\triangle ABC \sim \triangle DEC$ by SAS Similarity Theorem
**(C)** $\triangle ABC \sim \triangle DEC$ by SSS Similarity Theorem
**(D)** $\triangle ABC$ and $\triangle DEC$ are not similar.
**(E)** Answer cannot be determined.

**40.** Given: $\overline{AB} \parallel \overline{ED}$; $AC = 4$; $BC = 7$

**41.** Given: $AC = 4$; $DC = 6$; $BC = 6$; $EC = 9$

**42.** Given: $AC = 3$; $DC = 7$; $AB = 6$; $DE = 14$

**43.** Given: $AB = 9$; $BC = 12$; $AC = 15$; $DE = 15$;
$EC = 18$; $DC = 21$

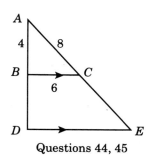

Questions 40–43

**44.** If $CE = 12$, then $BD = \underline{\ ?\ }$.
**(A)** 4      **(B)** 6
**(C)** 8      **(D)** 9

**45.** If $BD = 8$, then $DE = \underline{\ ?\ }$.
**(A)** 12      **(B)** 14
**(C)** 16      **(D)** 18

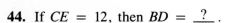

Questions 44, 45

**46.** In $\triangle DEF$, if $\overline{DE} \cong \overline{DF}$, $\overrightarrow{DX}$ bisects $\angle EDF$, and $X$ lies on $\overline{EF}$, then $m\angle DXE = \underline{\ ?\ }$.

**(A)** 120      **(B)** 70      **(C)** 80
**(D)** 90      **(E)** Answer cannot be determined.

**47.** In $\triangle RSQ$, if $\overrightarrow{ST}$ bisects $\angle QSR$, then $RT = \underline{\ ?\ }$.
**(A)** 6      **(B)** 9
**(C)** 12      **(D)** 15

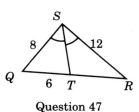

Question 47

**48.** In the given figure, the shortest segment is $\underline{\ ?\ }$.
**(A)** $\overline{AB}$      **(B)** $\overline{BC}$      **(C)** $\overline{BD}$
**(D)** $\overline{CD}$      **(E)** $\overline{AD}$

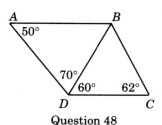

Question 48

**49.** If $\triangle QRS \sim \triangle XYZ$, $QR = 9$, $RS = 12$, $QS = 14$, and $YZ = 18$, then the scale factor of $\triangle QRS$ to $\triangle XYZ$ is $\underline{\ ?\ }$.
**(A)** $1:2$      **(B)** $2:3$      **(C)** $7:9$      **(D)** $3:4$      **(E)** none of these

**50.** If $\triangle ABC \sim \triangle DEF$, then $AB:DE = CB:\underline{\ ?\ }$.
**(A)** $DF$      **(B)** $DE$      **(C)** $FE$      **(D)** none of these

**Answers**

40. _____ (2)
41. _____ (2)
42. _____ (2)
43. _____ (2)
44. _____ (2)
45. _____ (2)
46. _____ (2)
47. _____ (2)
48. _____ (2)
49. _____ (2)
50. _____ (2)

NAME _____ DATE _____ SCORE _____

# Test 31  *Supplementary Test*

**Directions:** Write answers in the spaces provided.

Simplify.

**1.** $\sqrt{20}$  **2.** $2\sqrt{8}$  **3.** $\sqrt{\dfrac{5}{9}}$  **4.** $\sqrt{\dfrac{3}{10}}$

Find the geometric mean between the given numbers in simplest form.

**5.** 2 and 18  **6.** 6 and 12  **7.** $\dfrac{1}{2}$ and $\dfrac{2}{5}$

Each figure shows the altitude drawn to the hypotenuse of a right triangle. Find each value in simplest form.

**8. a.** Find $x$.  **9. a.** Find $y$.
   **b.** Find $w$.     **b.** Find $z$.

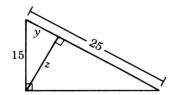

Use the right triangle shown to find each value in simplest form.

**10.** If $a = 8$ and $b = 6$, find $c$.

**11.** If $a = 6$ and $b = 3$, find $c$.

**12.** If $b = \sqrt{17}$ and $c = 9$, find $a$.

**Questions 10–12**

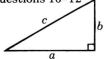

In Questions 13–15, find the value of $x$ in simplest form.

**13.**  **14.**  **15.**

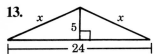 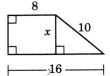 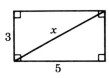

**16.** A side of a square has length 3. Find the length of a diagonal.

**17.** A diagonal of a square has length 8. Find the length of a side.

**18.** For the rectangular solid shown, find the length of $\overline{DF}$.

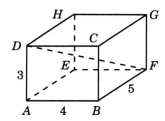

**Answers**

1. _____ (4)

2. _____ (4)

3. _____ (4)

4. _____ (4)

5. _____ (4)

6. _____ (4)

7. _____ (4)

8. a. _____ (5)

  b. _____ (5)

9. a. _____ (5)

  b. _____ (5)

10. _____ (5)

11. _____ (5)

12. _____ (5)

13. _____ (6)

14. _____ (6)

15. _____ (6)

16. _____ (6)

17. _____ (6)

18. _____ (7)

# Test 32    *Right Triangles*

Lessons 8-3, 8-4

**Directions:** Write answers in the spaces provided.

State whether a triangle with sides of the given lengths is acute, right, or obtuse.

**1.** 7, 8, 10

**2.** 6, 9, 11

**3.** $3n$, $4n$, $5n$ where $n > 0$

**4.** 4, 6, $2\sqrt{13}$

**5.** A right triangle has sides whose lengths are represented by $n^2 - 1$, $2n$, and $n^2 + 1$. If the length of the longer leg is 48, find the lengths of the shorter leg and the hypotenuse.

In Questions 6–11, find each value in simplest form.

**6. a.** Find $x$.
　 **b.** Find $y$.

**7. a.** Find $x$.
　 **b.** Find $y$.

**8. a.** Find $x$.
　 **b.** Find $y$.

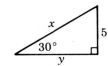

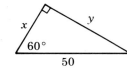

**9. a.** Find $x$.
　 **b.** Find $y$.

**10.** Find $x$.

**11. a.** Find $AC$.
　 **b.** Find $BD$.

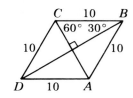

**12.** In $\triangle CDE$, $m \angle C = 90$, $m \angle D = 60$, and $m \angle E = 30$. Which side of the triangle is the longer leg?

Find each of the following in simplest form.

**13.** If $BD = 4$, find $AD$.

**14.** If $AC = 12$, find $BD$.

**15.** If $AB = 20$, find $CD$.

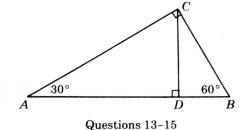

Questions 13–15

### Answers

1. _____ (4)

2. _____ (4)

3. _____ (4)

4. _____ (4)

5. _____ (6)

6. a. _____ (5)

　 b. _____ (5)

7. a. _____ (5)

　 b. _____ (5)

8. a. _____ (5)

　 b. _____ (5)

9. a. _____ (5)

　 b. _____ (5)

10. _____ (5)

11. a. _____ (5)

　 b. _____ (5)

12. _____ (5)

13. _____ (6)

14. _____ (6)

15. _____ (6)

# Test 33  *Trigonometry*

**Directions:** Write answers in the spaces provided.

In Questions 1–4, refer to the diagram at the right.

**1.** $\sin B = \dfrac{?}{?}$     **2.** $\cos A = \dfrac{?}{?}$

**3.** $\sin A = \dfrac{?}{?}$     **4.** $\tan A = \dfrac{?}{?}$

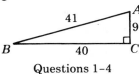

Questions 1–4

Find the *exact* value of each of the following.

**5.** $\sin 45°$     **6.** $\cos 30°$     **7.** $\tan 60°$

**8.** If $\sin A = \dfrac{1}{2}$, what is the measure of $\angle A$?

Use a calculator or the table on page 311 to find $x$ to the nearest tenth.

**9.**

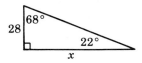

**10.**

Find $x°$ correct to the nearest degree.

**11.**

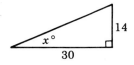

**12.**

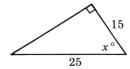

**13.** Find $x$ correct to the nearest integer.

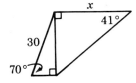

**14.** The base angles of an isosceles triangle are each 55°. The base is 40 cm long. Find the length of the altitude to the base to the nearest centimeter.

**15.** A tower casts a shadow 35 m long when the angle of elevation of the sun is 32°. How high is the tower to the nearest meter?

**Answers**

1. _____ (5)

2. _____ (5)

3. _____ (5)

4. _____ (5)

5. _____ (5)

6. _____ (5)

7. _____ (5)

8. _____ (5)

9. _____ (8)

10. _____ (8)

11. _____ (8)

12. _____ (8)

13. _____ (10)

14. _____ (9)

15. _____ (9)

# Test 34 *Chapter 8 Test*

**Directions:** Write answers in the spaces provided.

Simplify.

**1.** $\sqrt{28}$        **2.** $3\sqrt{45}$        **3.** $\dfrac{12}{\sqrt{3}}$

Find the geometric mean between the given numbers in simplest form.

**4.** 4 and 10                  **5.** 9 and 16

Refer to the diagram to find each value in simplest form.

**6.** If $r = 3$ and $s = 6$, find $h$.

**7.** If $b = 6$ and $c = 18$, find $r$.

**8.** If $r = 3$ and $c = 12$, find $a$.

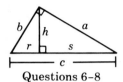

Questions 6–8

Use the right triangle shown to find each value in simplest form.

**9.** If $a = 4$ and $b = 5$, find $c$.

**10.** If $a = 16$ and $c = 20$, find $b$.

**11.** If $a = \sqrt{5}$ and $b = 2\sqrt{5}$, find $c$.

Questions 9–11

State whether the triangle with sides of the given lengths is acute, right, or obtuse.

**12.** 3, 5, 6          **13.** 1, 2, $\sqrt{5}$          **14.** 10, 10, 14

Find each value in simplest form.

**15. a.** Find $x$.
**b.** Find $y$.

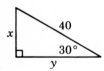

**16. a.** Find $x$.
**b.** Find $y$.

**17.** Find $x$.

**18.** Find $x$.

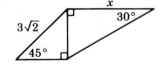

**Answers**

1. _____ (3)

2. _____ (3)

3. _____ (3)

4. _____ (3)

5. _____ (3)

6. _____ (4)

7. _____ (4)

8. _____ (4)

9. _____ (4)

10. _____ (4)

11. _____ (4)

12. _____ (3)

13. _____ (3)

14. _____ (3)

15. a. _____ (3)

    b. _____ (3)

16. a. _____ (3)

    b. _____ (3)

17. _____ (4)

18. _____ (4)

*(continued)*

TESTS for GEOMETRY

## Test 34 *(continued)*

**Answers**

**19.** The diagonals of a rhombus have lengths 4 and 12. Find the length of a side in simplest form.

**20.** The vertex angle of an isosceles triangle is 120°. The base length is 18. Find the length of the altitude to the base in simplest form.

In Questions 21–24, refer to the diagram at the right.

**21.** $\sin R = \frac{?}{?}$     **22.** $\sin T = \frac{?}{?}$

**23.** $\cos R = \frac{?}{?}$     **24.** $\tan T = \frac{?}{?}$

**Questions 21–24**

In Questions 25–27, write the letter of the equation that could be used to solve for $x$.

**25.** **(A)** $\sin 40° = \frac{x}{75}$     **(B)** $\tan 50° = \frac{x}{75}$

**(C)** $\cos 40° = \frac{x}{75}$     **(D)** $\cos 40° = \frac{75}{x}$

**26.** **(A)** $\tan 39° = \frac{x}{14}$     **(B)** $\cos 51° = \frac{x}{14}$

**(C)** $\sin 51° = \frac{14}{x}$     **(D)** $\tan 90° = \frac{18}{x}$

**27.** **(A)** $\tan x° = \frac{80}{100}$     **(B)** $\sin x° = \frac{80}{100}$

**(C)** $\cos x° = \frac{60}{80}$     **(D)** $\sin x° = \frac{100}{80}$

**Answers**

19. _____ (4)

20. _____ (4)

21. _____ (3)

22. _____ (3)

23. _____ (3)

24. _____ (3)

25. _____ (3)

26. _____ (3)

27. _____ (3)

28. _____ (3)

**28.** The angle of depression from the top of the tower to point $A$ is 23°. The distance from $A$ to the base $B$ of the tower is 80 m. To find the height, $h$, of the tower, use:

**(A)** $\sin 23° = \frac{h}{80}$     **(B)** $\cos 23° = \frac{80}{h}$     **(C)** $\tan 23° = \frac{h}{80}$

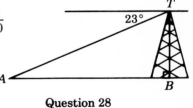

**Question 28**

---

**CHALLENGE (Optional)**

*ABCDEFGH* is a regular octagon with each side of length 2. Find *AF* and *AE*.

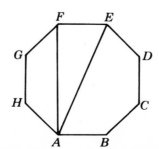

**ANSWER**

_____

_____

---

# Test 35  Tangents, Arcs, and Chords

**Directions:** Write answers in the spaces provided.

In Questions 1–3, the diameter of $\odot O$ is 14. State whether each point is inside, outside, or on $\odot O$.

1. $OC = 14$. Where is $C$?    2. $OD = 7$. Where is $D$?

3. $OE = 3.5$. Where is $E$?

4. If $M$ and $N$ are points on $\odot A$, then $\overline{MN}$ is a(n) __?__ of $\odot A$.

5. If $RS + ST = RT$ and $R$ and $S$ are on $\odot P$, then $\overleftrightarrow{RT}$ is a(n) __?__ of $\odot P$.

6. In a plane, if $X$ is the only point of line $l$ that is on $\odot O$, then $l$ is __?__ to $\odot O$.

7. $\overline{RT}$ is tangent to $\odot O$ and $\odot P$. If $OR = 9$, $PS = 6$, and $ST = 15$, find the value of $RT$.

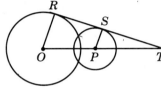

8. Two coplanar circles are externally tangent. How many common tangents can be drawn to the two circles?

9. Name a minor arc.

10. Name a major arc

11. If $m\overset{\frown}{SX} = 40$, find $m\angle 1$

12. If $m\angle 1 = 30$, find $m\overset{\frown}{XRS}$.

13. If $m\overset{\frown}{XSR} = 210$, find $m\angle 2$.

14. If $m\angle 1 = 20$, find $m\overset{\frown}{XR}$.

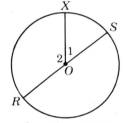

Questions 9–14

In Questions 15–19, $O$ is the center of the circle and $\overline{AB} \perp \overline{CD}$.

15. If $AB = 20$ and $CD = 12$, find $OE$.

16. If $OA = 13$ and $EA = 1$, find $CD$.

17. If $m\overset{\frown}{BC} = 150$, find $m\overset{\frown}{AD}$.

18. If $m\overset{\frown}{ABD} = 320$, find $m\overset{\frown}{CD}$.

19. If $m\angle AOC = 30$ and $OC = 12$, find $OE$.

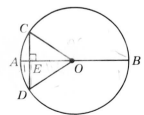

Questions 15–19

**Answers**

1. _____ (5)
2. _____ (5)
3. _____ (5)
4. _____ (5)
5. _____ (5)
6. _____ (5)
7. _____ (5)
8. _____ (5)
9. _____ (5)
10. _____ (5)
11. _____ (5)
12. _____ (5)
13. _____ (5)
14. _____ (5)
15. _____ (6)
16. _____ (6)
17. _____ (6)
18. _____ (6)
19. _____ (6)

## Test 38 *(continued)*

7. Construct a rhombus with sides of length *m* and acute angles congruent to $\angle P$.

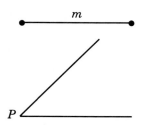

8. Construct an angle with measure 45 and vertex at *X*.

9. The medians of the triangle are shown.
   a. Find the value of *x*.
   b. Find the value of *y*.

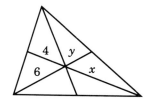

10. State whether the point of concurrency for each set of lines is *inside*, *on*, or *outside* the triangle.
    a. the lines containing the altitudes of an acute triangle
    b. the lines containing the medians of an obtuse triangle
    c. the lines containing the perpendicular bisectors of the sides of a right triangle

# Test 39   *More Constructions*

**Directions:** Do constructions in the spaces provided.

1. Construct a tangent to $\odot O$ through $X$.

2. Construct a tangent to $\odot O$ through $Y$.

### Answers

1. (See question) _____ (17)

2. (See question) _____ (17)

3. (See question) _____ (22)

4. (See question) _____ (22)

5. (See question) _____ (22)

3. Inscribe a circle in $\triangle JKL$.

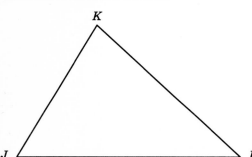

4. Construct a segment of length $x$ such that $\frac{c}{b} = \frac{a}{x}$.

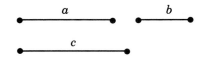

5. Construct an equilateral triangle with perimeter equal to $s$.

NAME _____ DATE _____ SCORE _____

# Test 40 Locus

**Directions:** Write answers in the spaces provided.

In Questions 1–5, describe each locus of points completely.

**1.** In a plane, the locus of points 3 cm from a given line *m*

_____

**2.** In a plane, the locus of points equidistant from the sides of a given angle, $\angle RST$

_____

**3.** In a plane, the locus of points equidistant from two given parallel lines *e* and *f*

_____

**4.** In space, the locus of points 5 cm from a given point *H*

_____

**5.** In a plane, the locus of the midpoints of all radii of a circle with center *O* and radius 8

_____

**Answers**

1. _(See question)_ (9)

2. _(See question)_ (9)

3. _(See question)_ (9)

4. _(See question)_ (9)

5. _(See question)_ (9)

6. _____ (9)

7. _____ (9)

8. _____ (9)

9. _(See question)_ (13)

10. _(See question)_ (15)

In Questions 6–8, write the *number* of points that satisfy the conditions in each problem. All problems are restricted to a plane. If the number of points cannot be determined, write *cannot tell*.

**6.** Line *t* is a transversal of parallel lines *l* and *m*. The locus of points 1 cm from *t* and equidistant from *l* and *m*

**7.** Point *P* is 5 cm from line *l*. The locus of points 8 cm from *P* and 3 cm from *l*

**8.** *A*, *B*, and *C* are collinear with $AB + BC = AC$ and $AB = 6$. The locus of points equidistant from *A* and *B* and 3 cm from *C*

**9.** Construct and label the locus of points equidistant from *l* and *m*.

**10.** Given $\odot O$ and $\overline{AB}$. Construct and label the locus of midpoints of all chords of $\odot O$ with length *AB*.

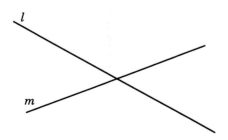

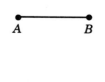

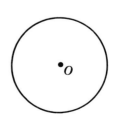

# Test 41   *Chapter 10 Test*

**Directions:** Write answers in the spaces provided.

In Questions 1–4, do the indicated construction.

**1.** Construct the median from *T*.

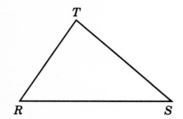

**2.** Circumscribe a circle about △*DEF*.

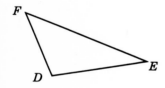

**3.** *M* and *N* are points of tangency. Locate point *L* on $\overrightarrow{JM}$ by construction so that ⊙*O* is inscribed in △*JKL*.

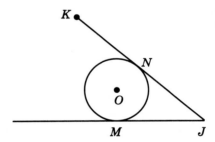

**4.** Construct $\overline{XY}$ such that *XY* is the geometric mean between *a* and *b*.

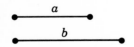

*(continued)*

## Test 41 *(continued)*

In Questions 5–7, describe each locus of points completely.

**5.** In space, the locus of points equidistant from two parallel planes

_____

_____

**6.** In a plane, the locus of points 4 cm from the center of a circle whose radius is 5 cm

_____

_____

**7.** In a plane, the locus of the centers of all circles with radius 3 cm that are tangent to a given line *l*.

_____

_____

**Answers**

5. (See question) _____ (8)

6. (See question) _____ (8)

7. (See question) _____ (8)

8. a. (See question) _____ (5)

   b. (See question) _____ (5)

   c. (See question) _____ (5)

9. (See question) _____ (13)

**8.** Given ∠*ABC*, there are three possibilities for the locus of points in a plane equidistant from the sides of ∠*ABC* and at a distance, *d*, from a point *P*. Draw diagrams to illustrate each possibility.

**a.** 1 point          **b.** 2 points          **c.** 0 points

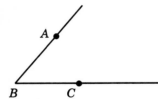  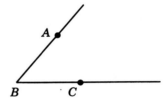

**9.** Given a segment $\overline{AB}$, construct and label the locus of points at a distance *AB* from point *A* and equidistant from *A* and *B*.

_____

**CHALLENGE (Optional)**

It can be proved that the following three points in any triangle are collinear.
1. The intersection of the medians
2. The intersection of the lines containing the altitudes
3. The intersection of the perpendicular bisectors of the sides

The line containing the three points is called *Euler's line* of the triangle.
Sketch and label Euler's line for △*ABC*.

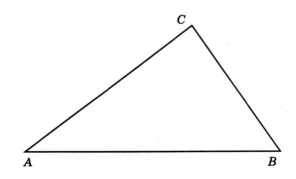

# Test 42 *Cumulative Test, Chapters 8–10*

**Directions:** Write answers in the spaces provided.

In Questions 1–3, state whether the triangle with sides of the given lengths is acute, right, or obtuse.

**1.** 5, 8, 9        **2.** 4, 8, $\sqrt{35}$        **3.** $2\sqrt{10}$, 7, 3

**4.** Find the geometric mean of 5 and 15.

In Questions 5–10, find the value of each variable in simplest form.

**5.** If $a = 7$ and $b = 8$, find $c$.

**6.** If $x = 5$ and $y = 8$, find $h$.

Questions 5–8

**7.** If $a = 10$ and $c = 20$, find $x$.

**8.** If $y = 6$ and $c = 10$, find $b$.

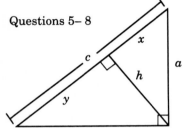

**9. a.** Find $w$.
   **b.** Find $x$.

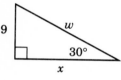

**10. a.** Find $y$.
    **b.** Find $z$.

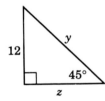

In Questions 11–13, refer to the diagram below.

**11.** $\sin R = \dfrac{?}{?}$

**12.** $\tan R = \dfrac{?}{?}$

**13.** $\cos P = \dfrac{?}{?}$

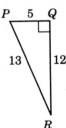

Write the letter of the equation that could be used to solve for $x$.

**14. (A)** $\tan 20° = \dfrac{16}{x}$   **(B)** $\sin 20° = \dfrac{16}{x}$      **15. (A)** $\sin 35° = \dfrac{10}{x}$   **(B)** $\sin 35° = \dfrac{x}{10}$

     **(C)** $\cos 20° = \dfrac{16}{x}$   **(D)** $\cos 70° = \dfrac{x}{16}$           **(C)** $\cos 55° = \dfrac{10}{x}$   **(D)** $\tan 35° = \dfrac{10}{x}$

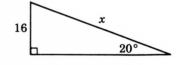

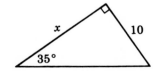

**Answers**

1. _____ (2)

2. _____ (2)

3. _____ (2)

4. _____ (2)

5. _____ (3)

6. _____ (3)

7. _____ (3)

8. _____ (3)

9. a. _____ (2)

   b. _____ (2)

10. a. _____ (2)

    b. _____ (2)

11. _____ (2)

12. _____ (2)

13. _____ (2)

14. _____ (3)

15. _____ (3)

*(continued)*

## Test 42 *(continued)*

Given ⊙ O, sketch each figure.

**16.** The radius that contains A

**17.** The tangent that contains B

**18.** The chord that contains C and A

**19.** The diameter that contains B

**20.** The secant that contains B and D

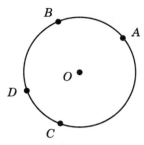
Questions 16–20

In Questions 21–26, $\overline{AB}$ is tangent to ⊙O at B, $m\widehat{CD} = 60$, $m\widehat{EF} = 40$, and $m\widehat{BC} = 80$. Find each measure.

**21.** $m \angle 1$

**22.** $m \angle 2$

**23.** $m \angle 3$

**24.** $m \angle 4$

**25.** $m \angle 5$

**26.** $m \angle 6$

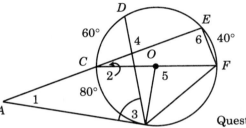
Questions 21–26

In Questions 27–29, refer to the diagram at the right.

**27.** $\overline{AB}$ is tangent to the circle. If $AC = 4$ and $GC = 11$, then $AB = \underline{\ ?\ }$.

**28.** If $CE = 2$, $DE = 3$, and $EB = 6$, then $EG = \underline{\ ?\ }$.

**29.** If $AC = 4$, $CG = 11$, and $AD = 5$, then $DF = \underline{\ ?\ }$.

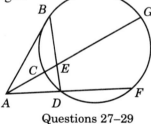
Questions 27–29

Given ⊙ O, $\overline{CA} \perp \overline{BD}$, $m\widehat{BC} = 120$, and $AC = 16$. Find each measure.

**30.** $m\widehat{CD}$

**31.** $m \angle BOA$

**32.** $EO$

**33.** $m\widehat{BD}$

**34.** $BD$

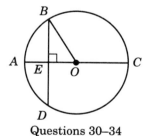
Questions 30–34

### Answers

**16.** (See question) _____ (1)

**17.** (See question) _____ (1)

**18.** (See question) _____ (1)

**19.** (See question) _____ (1)

**20.** (See question) _____ (1)

**21.** _____ (2)

**22.** _____ (2)

**23.** _____ (2)

**24.** _____ (2)

**25.** _____ (2)

**26.** _____ (2)

**27.** _____ (3)

**28.** _____ (3)

**29.** _____ (3)

**30.** _____ (1)

**31.** _____ (1)

**32.** _____ (1)

**33.** _____ (1)

**34.** _____ (2)

*(continued)*

## Test 42 *(continued)*

In Questions 35–37, describe each locus of points completely.

**35.** In a plane, the locus of points 3 cm from a given point *G*

_____

**36.** In a plane, the locus of points equidistant from points *A* and *B*.

_____

**37.** In space, the locus of points 2 cm from plane *X*

_____

**38.** Draw two parallel lines *r* and *s*. Then place a point *K* so that the locus of points in a plane equidistant from *r* and *s* and 1 cm from *K* is:

  **a.** 1 point         **b.** 2 points         **c.** 0 points

**Answers**

**35.** _(See question)_ (3)

**36.** _(See question)_ (3)

**37.** _(See question)_ (3)

**38. a.** (See question) (1)

    **b.** (See question) (1)

    **c.** (See question) (1)

**39.** _(See question)_ (4)

**40.** _(See question)_ (4)

**41.** _(See question)_ (4)

**42.** _(See question)_ (4)

**39.** Construct the altitude to the hypotenuse of △*ABC*.

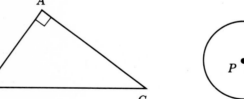

**40.** Construct a tangent to ⊙*P* from point *K*.

        ● *K*

**41.** Circumscribe a circle about △*DEF*.

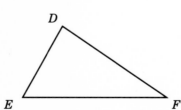

**42.** Find by construction point *R* on $\overline{QS}$ such that $QR : RS = 1 : 2$.

# Test 43   *Areas of Polygons*

Lessons 11-1 through 11-4

**Directions:** Write answers in the spaces provided.

**Answers**

1. Use dashed lines to show three different ways the given figure can be divided into four triangles that do not overlap.

1. (See question) _____ (3)

In Questions 2–9, find the area of each figure.

2. A rectangle with base 5 and height 12

3. A parallelogram with base 9 and height 4

4. A triangle with base 11 and height 8

5. A square with perimeter 28

6. A trapezoid with bases 6 and 15 and height 12

7. A rhombus with diagonals of lengths 18 and 30

8. A regular polygon with apothem 9 and perimeter 40

9. An isosceles triangle with sides of lengths 10, 10, and 12

10. The area of a square is 50. Find the length of a diagonal.

11. A rectangle has width represented by $x$ and length represented by $4x$. If the area of the rectangle is 80, find the value of $x$.

In Questions 12–16, find the area of each figure.
In Question 17, find *CF*.

2. _____ (5)

3. _____ (5)

4. _____ (5)

5. _____ (5)

6. _____ (5)

7. _____ (5)

8. _____ (5)

9. _____ (5)

10. _____ (7)

11. _____ (7)

12. _____ (7)

13. _____ (7)

14. _____ (7)

15. _____ (7)

16. _____ (7)

17. _____ (8)

12.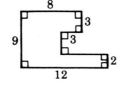

13.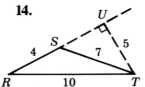

14.

15.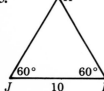

16.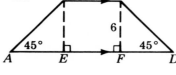

17.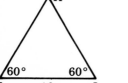

# Test 44  *Supplementary Test*

**Lessons 11-5, 11-6**

**Directions:** Write answers in the spaces provided.

1. Which ratio represents the number $\pi$?

   **(A)** diameter : radius      **(B)** diameter : circumference
   **(C)** circumference : diameter      **(D)** circumference : radius

2. The radius of a circle is 9.
   **a.** Find the circumference in terms of $\pi$.
   **b.** Find the area in terms of $\pi$.

3. The diameter of a circle is 22. Use $\pi \approx 3.14$.
   **a.** Find the circumference to the nearest tenth.
   **b.** Find the area to the nearest tenth.

4. The area of a circle is $20\pi$. Find the radius in simplest form.

5. A central angle of a circle has measure 50. The radius of the circle is 18. Find the area of the sector in the interior of the angle in terms of $\pi$.

6. A circle has a radius of 12. If an arc of the circle has measure 100, find the length of the arc in terms of $\pi$.

7. In a circle, the length of an arc with measure 120 is $14\pi$. Find the radius of the circle.

8. In terms of $\pi$, how much farther does a 70 cm diameter bicycle tire travel in one revolution than a 50 cm diameter bicycle tire?

Find the area of each shaded region in terms of $\pi$. Point $O$ marks the center of a circle.

## Answers

1. _____ (5)

2. a. _____ (5)

   b. _____ (5)

3. a. _____ (5)

   b. _____ (5)

4. _____ (6)

5. _____ (7)

6. _____ (7)

7. _____ (7)

8. _____ (8)

9. _____ (8)

10. _____ (8)

11. _____ (8)

12. _____ (8)

13. _____ (8)

9.
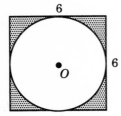

10.
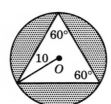

11.
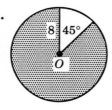

12.
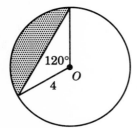

13.
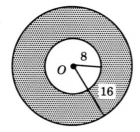

TESTS for GEOMETRY

# Test 45  *Circles, Similar Figures, and Geometric Probability*

**Answers**

**Directions:** Write answers in the spaces provided.

1. The diameter of a circle is 10. Find the area of the circle to the nearest tenth. Use $\pi \approx 3.14$.

2. The radius of a circle is 12. Find the circumference of the circle in terms of $\pi$.

3. The area of a circle is $40\pi$. Find the radius of the circle in simplest form.

4. In a circle with radius 15, the measure of an arc is 150. Find the length of the arc in terms of $\pi$.

Find the area of each shaded region in terms of $\pi$. Points $O$ and $P$ mark the centers of the circles.

5.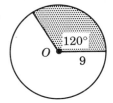

6.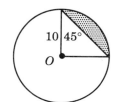

7.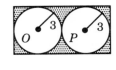

8. The radii of two circles are 6 and 10.
   a. What is the scale factor of the circles?
   b. What is the ratio of the areas of the circles?

9. $\triangle RST \sim \triangle JKL$, $RS = 8$, $ST = 12$, $RT = 18$, $KL = 16$
   a. What is the ratio of the perimeters of the triangles?
   b. What is the ratio of the areas of the triangles?

In Questions 10 and 11, find each ratio.

10. $\dfrac{\text{area of } \triangle ABC}{\text{area of } \triangle DEC}$

11. $\dfrac{\text{area of } \triangle DEC}{\text{area of trapezoid } ABED}$

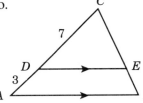

12. $B$ is the midpoint of $\overline{AC}$ and $BD = DE = EC$. If a point $X$ is selected at random from $\overline{AC}$, what is the probability that:
   a. $X$ is on $\overline{AB}$?          b. $X$ is on $\overline{DB}$?

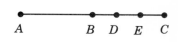

13. A point is randomly chosen inside the square at the right. The measure of central angle $O$ is 18.
   a. In terms of $\pi$, what is the probability that the point is inside the shaded sector?
   b. If 80 points are chosen, estimate the number inside the shaded sector.

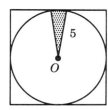

| | |
|---|---|
| 1. _____ (6) | |
| 2. _____ (6) | |
| 3. _____ (6) | |
| 4. _____ (6) | |
| 5. _____ (6) | |
| 6. _____ (6) | |
| 7. _____ (6) | |
| 8. a. _____ (5) | |
| b. _____ (6) | |
| 9. a. _____ (5) | |
| b. _____ (6) | |
| 10. _____ (6) | |
| 11. _____ (6) | |
| 12. a. _____ (6) | |
| b. _____ (6) | |
| 13. a. _____ (6) | |
| b. _____ (6) | |

# Test 46  *Chapter 11 Test*

**Answers**

**Directions:** Write answers in the spaces provided.

In Questions 1–10, find the area of each figure.

1. A rectangle with base 10 and height 16

2. A triangle with base 18 and height 3

3. A trapezoid with bases 5 and 15 and height 9

4. A regular hexagon with side 4

5. An isosceles triangle with sides 13, 13, and 24

6. A circle with radius 14

7.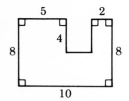

8.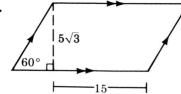

9.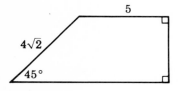

10.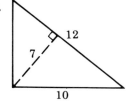

1. _____ (3)

2. _____ (3)

3. _____ (4)

4. _____ (5)

5. _____ (5)

6. _____ (5)

7. _____ (5)

8. _____ (5)

9. _____ (5)

10. _____ (5)

11. _____ (5)

12. _____ (5)

13. _____ (5)

14. _____ (5)

15. _____ (5)

11. The area of a circle is $64\pi$. Find the radius.

12. The base of a triangle is three times its height. The area is 216 cm². Find the length of the base.

13. Refer to the diagram at the right. Find the length of $\overarc{AB}$ in terms of $\pi$.

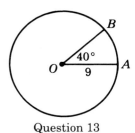

Question 13

Find the area of each shaded region in terms of $\pi$. Point $O$ marks the center of the circle.

14.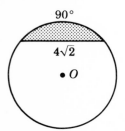

15.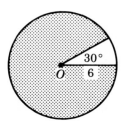

*(continued)*

## Test 46 *(continued)*

**Answers**

**16.** The scale factor of two similar polygons is $2:7$. What is the ratio of their areas?

**17.** The scale factor of two circles is $3:2$. The area of the larger circle is $81\pi$. Find the area of the smaller circle.

**18.** The areas of two regular hexagons are $54\sqrt{3}$ and $150\sqrt{3}$, respectively. What is the ratio of their perimeters?

**19.** In the figure, $AB = BC = CD$ and $BE = EC$. If a point $Z$ is picked at random on $\overline{AD}$, what is the probability that:
  **a.** $Z$ is between $A$ and $B$?
  **b.** $Z$ is between $B$ and $E$?
  **c.** $Z$ is between $E$ and $D$?

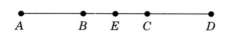

**20.** A target has circles with radii of 2 cm, 10 cm, and 20 cm, as shown. What is the probability that a dart that randomly hits the target will hit within:
  **a.** the 2 cm circle?
  **b.** the outer ring?

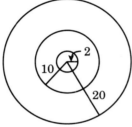

**21.** During the rush period at a certain train station, every 15 minutes an express train arrives and waits 4 minutes to pick up passengers. Four minutes after the express train leaves, a local train arrives and waits 3 minutes to pick up passengers. If a passenger arrives at the station at a random time during the rush period, find the probability of each of the following.
  **a.** The express train will be waiting at the station.
  **b.** No train will be waiting at the station.

16. _____ (5)

17. _____ (5)

18. _____ (5)

19. a. _____ (2)

    b. _____ (2)

    c. _____ (2)

20. a. _____ (2)

    b. _____ (2)

21. a. _____ (3)

    b. _____ (2)

---

**CHALLENGE (Optional)**

Find the area of the shaded region in terms of $\pi$. $O$ and $P$ are the centers of the circles.

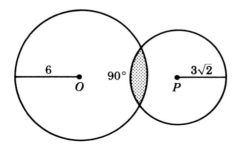

**ANSWER**

_____

# Test 47  *Important Solids*

Lessons 12-1 through 12-3

**Directions:** Write answers in the spaces provided.

**Answers**

In Questions 1–5, refer to the diagram shown. Complete each statement.

1. The solid is a right  ? prism.

2. *ABGF* is a(n)  ? of the prism.

3. *ABCDE* is a(n)  ? of the prism.

4. $\overline{FA}$ is a(n)  ? of the prism.

5. *GB* is the  ? of the prism.

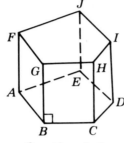

Questions 1–5

In Questions 6–10, *JK* = *KL* = *LM* = *MJ*. Complete each statement.

6. The solid is a(n)  ? pyramid.

7. $\overline{JK}$ is a(n)  ? of the pyramid.

8. $\overline{VK}$ is a(n)  ? of the pyramid.

9. *VP* is the  ? of the pyramid.

10. *VX* is the  ? of the pyramid.

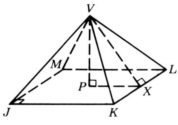

Questions 6–10

11. A right triangular prism has height 8 and base edges 3, 4, and 5.
    a. Find the lateral area.
    b. Find the total area.
    c. Find the volume.

12. A regular square pyramid has height 8 and base edge 12.
    a. Find the slant height.
    b. Find the length of a lateral edge.
    c. Find the lateral area.
    d. Find the volume.

In Questions 13 and 14, leave your answers in terms of $\pi$ when appropriate.

13. The radius of a cylinder is 3 and the height is 6.
    a. Find the lateral area.
    b. Find the total area.
    c. Find the volume.

14. The radius of a cone is 5 and the height is 12.
    a. Find the slant height.
    b. Find the lateral area.
    c. Find the total area
    d. Find the volume.

1. _____ (3)

2. _____ (3)

3. _____ (3)

4. _____ (3)

5. _____ (3)

6. _____ (3)

7. _____ (3)

8. _____ (3)

9. _____ (3)

10. _____ (3)

11. a. _____ (5)

b. _____ (5)

c. _____ (5)

12. a. _____ (5)

b. _____ (5)

c. _____ (5)

d. _____ (5)

13. a. _____ (5)

b. _____ (5)

c. _____ (5)

14. a. _____ (5)

b. _____ (5)

c. _____ (5)

d. _____ (5)

# Test 48 *Similar Solids*

**Directions:** Write answers in the spaces provided.

In Questions 1–5, leave your answers in terms of $\pi$ when appropriate.

1. The radius of a sphere is 6.
   a. Find the area.
   b. Find the volume.

2. The radius of a sphere is $\frac{3}{2}$.
   a. Find the area.
   b. Find the volume.

3. The volume of a sphere is $36\pi$. Find the radius.

4. The area of a sphere is $16\pi$. Find the volume.

5. Find the area of the circle formed by the intersection of a plane and a sphere of radius 4 cm when the plane passes 3 cm from the center of the sphere.

6. The radii of two spheres are 4 and 2.
   a. The area of the first is __?__ times the area of the second.
   b. The volume of the first is __?__ times the volume of the second.

7. The radii of two cylinders are 5 and 3. Their heights are 30 and 18. Are the cylinders similar?

8. The scale factor of two similar pyramids is $1 : 3$.
   a. Find the ratio of the base perimeters.
   b. Find the ratio of the lateral areas.
   c. Find the ratio of the slant heights.
   d. Find the ratio of the volumes.

9. A plane parallel to the base of a cone divides the cone into two pieces. Find the ratios of the following:
   a. The lateral area of the top part of the cone to that of the whole cone
   b. The lateral area of the top part to that of the bottom part of the cone
   c. The volume of the top part of the cone to that of the whole cone
   d. The volume of the top part to that of the bottom part of the cone

**Answers**

1. a. _____ (7)

   b. _____ (7)

2. a. _____ (7)

   b. _____ (7)

3. _____ (7)

4. _____ (7)

5. _____ (7)

6. a. _____ (4)

   b. _____ (4)

7. _____ (3)

8. a. _____ (5)

   b. _____ (5)

   c. _____ (5)

   d. _____ (5)

9. a. _____ (5)

   b. _____ (5)

   c. _____ (5)

   d. _____ (5)

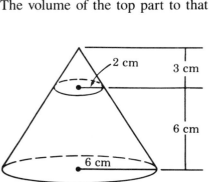

NAME _____ DATE _____ SCORE _____

# Test 49  *Chapter 12 Test*

**Directions:** Write answers in the spaces provided.

In Questions 1 and 2, refer to the right rectangular prism shown.

1. Find the total area.

2. Find the volume.

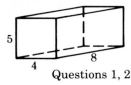

4  8
5
Questions 1, 2

3. A right trapezoidal prism has a base perimeter 22 cm, base area 24 cm², and height 10 cm.
   a. Find the lateral area.
   b. Find the volume.

4. The total area of a cube is 150 cm².
   a. Find the length of an edge.
   b. Find the volume.

5. A regular square pyramid has a base edge 6 and height 4.
   a. Find the slant height.
   b. Find the length of a lateral edge.
   c. Find the lateral area.
   d. Find the volume.

In Questions 6–8, leave your answers in terms of $\pi$ when appropriate.

6. The radius of a cylinder is 6 and the height is 2.
   a. Find the lateral area.
   b. Find the volume.

7. The volume of a cylinder is $125\pi$ and the radius is equal to the height. Find the lateral area.

8. The radius of a cone is 3 and the height is 9.
   a. Find the slant height.
   b. Find the lateral area.
   c. Find the volume.

9. If the radius of a cone is multiplied by 3 and the height remains the same, then the volume is multiplied by __?__ .

10. If the height of a cone is multiplied by 3 and the radius remains the same, then the volume is multiplied by __?__ .

| | |
|---|---|
| 1. _____ | (4) |
| 2. _____ | (4) |
| 3. a. _____ | (4) |
| b. _____ | (4) |
| 4. a. _____ | (4) |
| b. _____ | (4) |
| 5. a. _____ | (4) |
| b. _____ | (4) |
| c. _____ | (4) |
| d. _____ | (4) |
| 6. a. _____ | (4) |
| b. _____ | (4) |
| 7. _____ | (6) |
| 8. a. _____ | (4) |
| b. _____ | (4) |
| c. _____ | (4) |
| 9. _____ | (3) |
| 10. _____ | (3) |

*(continued)*

## Test 49 *(continued)*

**11.** If the radius of a cone is doubled and the height is multiplied by 3, then the volume is multiplied by __?__ .

For Questions 12–15, leave your answers in terms of $\pi$ when appropriate.

**12.** The radius of a sphere is 10.
   **a.** Find the area.
   **b.** Find the volume.

**13.** The volume of a hemisphere is $144\pi$. Find the radius.

**14.** Two similar pyramids have heights 9 and 12.
   **a.** Find the ratio of the lateral areas.
   **b.** Find the ratio of the volumes.

**15.** Two similar cones have volumes $24\pi$ and $81\pi$. If the lateral area of the smaller is $32\pi$, find the lateral area of the larger cone.

**Answers**

11. _____ (3)

12. a. _____ (4)

   b. _____ (4)

13. _____ (5)

14. a. _____ (3)

   b. _____ (3)

15. _____ (6)

---

**CHALLENGE (Optional)**

A cylindrical water tank with radius 2 feet and length 6 feet is filled with water to a depth of 3 feet when in a horizontal position. If the tank is turned upright, what is the depth of the water? Give your answer in terms of $\pi$.

**ANSWER**

_____

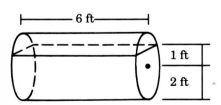

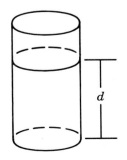

---

# Test 50   *Cumulative Test, Chapters 11–12*

**Directions:** Write answers in the spaces provided.

In Questions 1–14, find the area of each figure.

1. A rectangle with base 10 and height 6

2. A triangle with height 9 cm and base 8 cm

3. A trapezoid with bases 12 and 17 and height 6

4. A circle with radius 12 ft

5. A regular polygon with perimeter 24 and apothem 3

6. A rhombus with diagonals 8 in. and 12 in.

7. A square with sides of $3\sqrt{2}$ m

8. A sector of a circle with radius 9 and central angle with measure 120

**Answers**

1. _____ (2)
2. _____ (2)
3. _____ (2)
4. _____ (2)
5. _____ (2)
6. _____ (2)
7. _____ (2)
8. _____ (3)
9. _____ (2)
10. _____ (2)
11. _____ (2)
12. _____ (2)
13. _____ (2)
14. _____ (2)

9.
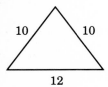

10.
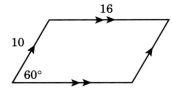

11.
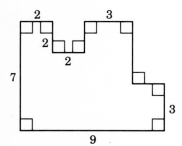

12.
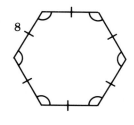

13.
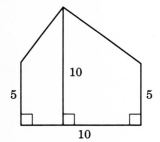

14.
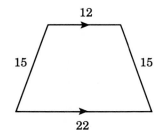

*(continued)*

TESTS for GEOMETRY

## Test 50 *(continued)*

**Answers**

**15.** Find the length of a 120° arc in a circle with radius 9.

15. _____ (3)

**16.** Find the area of the shaded region shown at the right. *O* is the center of the circle.

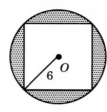

16. _____ (3)

17. a. _____ (3)

   b. _____ (3)

   c. _____ (3)

**17.** In the regular square pyramid shown, the base edge is 12 and the height is 8.
   **a.** Find the slant height.
   **b.** Find the lateral area.
   **c.** Find the volume.

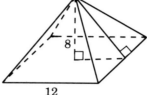

18. a. _____ (3)

   b. _____ (3)

19. a. _____ (3)

   b. _____ (3)

20. a. _____ (3)

   b. _____ (3)

**18.** An oil storage tank installed at a refinery is a right cylinder with diameter 18 m and height 10 m.
   **a.** The tank rests on the ground. Find the surface area of the tank that can be painted.
   **b.** The tank is half full of oil. Find the volume of the oil in the tank.

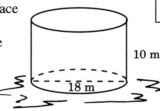

**19.** A soap bubble made by a child's bubble wand forms a sphere with a radius of 3 cm.
   **a.** Find the area.     **b.** Find the volume.

**20.** A right prism has lateral edges of length 10 cm and bases that are equilateral triangles with sides of length 8 cm.
   **a.** Find the total area.     **b.** Find the volume.

*(continued)*

## Test 50 *(continued)*

**Answers**

21. A local police department orders orange traffic cones with a diameter at the base of 14 in. and a height of 24 in.
   **a.** Find the slant height of a cone.
   **b.** Find the lateral area of a cone.
   **c.** Find the volume of a cone.

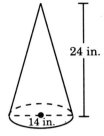

24 in.

14 in.

22. A regular square pyramid with height 8 m is intersected by a plane parallel to the base and 2 m above the base.
   **a.** Find the ratio of the volume of the top part to that of the whole pyramid.
   **b.** Find the ratio of the volume of the top part to that of the bottom part.
   **c.** Find the ratio of the lateral area of the top part to that of the whole pyramid.

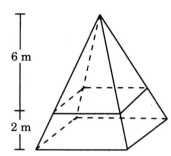

6 m

2 m

21. a. _____ (3)

   b. _____ (3)

   c. _____ (3)

22. a. _____ (3)

   b. _____ (3)

   c. _____ (3)

23. _____ (3)

24. _____ (4)

25. _____ (4)

26. a. _____ (3)

   b. _____ (3)

   c. _____ (3)

23. If the cost for materials to make a circular metal disk 3 cm in diameter is $.15, what would be the cost for materials to make a disk of the same thickness but 6 cm in diameter?

24. The perimeters of two similar polygons are 36 and 48. If the area of the larger polygon is 96, find the area of the smaller polygon.

25. If the height of a cone is tripled and the radius is doubled, then the volume of the new cone is __?__ times the volume of the original cone.

26. A square dart board 60 cm on a side has a square baseball field 40 cm on a side and 4 smaller squares each 10 cm on a side as targets, as shown. If a dart lands at a random point on the dart board, what is the probability that the dart:
   **a.** hits within the baseball field?
   **b.** hits within one of the 4 smaller squares?
   **c.** misses all five target squares?

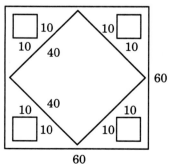

10   10

10   40   10

40   60

10   10
10   10

60

# Test 51 *Supplementary Test*

**Directions:** Write answers in the spaces provided.

**Answers**

1. State the coordinates of $C$ in terms of the coordinates of $A$ and $B$.

2. Express the distance from $A$ to $C$ in terms of coordinates.

3. Express the distance from $B$ to $C$ in terms of coordinates.

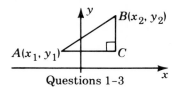

Questions 1–3

In Questions 4–7, find the distance between the points named.

4. $(5, 2)$ and $(-8, 2)$

5. $(1, 4)$ and $(5, 7)$

6. $(-2, 3)$ and $(-4, -1)$

7. $(e, f)$ and $(m, n)$

8. Given points $A(1, -2)$, $B(5, 0)$, and $C(1, 3)$. Tell whether $\triangle ABC$ is scalene, isosceles, or equilateral.

Find the center and the radius of each circle.

9. $(x - 8)^2 + (y + 2)^2 = 81$

10. $x^2 + y^2 = 12$

Write an equation of each circle described.

11. Center $(-2, 5)$ and radius 6 _____

12. Center $(2, -1)$ and passes through $(5, 3)$ _____

In Questions 13–16, find the slope of the line through the points named. If the slope of the line is not defined, write *not defined*.

13. $(3, 0)$; $(7, -5)$

14. $(3, 7)$; $(3, -4)$

15. $(2, -4)$; $(-1, -4)$

16. $(-1, 1)$; $(0, -8)$

17. A line with slope $\frac{2}{5}$ passes through the points $(-4, 1)$ and $(6, \underline{?})$.

18. The slope of line $l$ is $\frac{5}{4}$.
   a. The slope of any line parallel to $l$ is $\underline{?}$.
   b. The slope of any line perpendicular to $l$ is $\underline{?}$.

19. Sketch each line described.
   a. The line, $l$, passes through $(2, -1)$ and has slope $-\frac{2}{3}$.
   b. The line, $m$, passes through $(-1, -2)$ and is perpendicular to line $l$.

**Answers**

1. _____ (3)

2. _____ (4)

3. _____ (4)

4. _____ (5)

5. _____ (5)

6. _____ (5)

7. _____ (5)

8. _____ (7)

9. _____ (5)

10. _____ (5)

11. (See question) ____ (5)

12. (See question) ____ (5)

13. _____ (4)

14. _____ (4)

15. _____ (4)

16. _____ (4)

17. _____ (5)

18. a. _____ (5)

    b. _____ (5)

19. a. (See question) ____ (5)

    b. (See question) ____ (6)

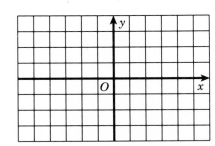

# Test 52  *Geometry and Algebra*

Lessons 13-4, 13-5

**Directions:** Write answers in the spaces provided.

**Answers**

1. A vector is a quantity that has both magnitude and __?__ .

1. _____ (3)

2. Moves on a game board may be represented as vectors. If a piece in a game moves from $R(2, 7)$ to $S(5, 1)$, then:

   **a.** $\overrightarrow{RS} = (\underline{\ ?\ }, \underline{\ ?\ })$.    **b.** $|\overrightarrow{RS}| = \underline{\ ?\ }$ .

2. a. _____ (4)

   b. _____ (4)

Name each vector as an ordered pair.

**3.** $\overrightarrow{AB} = (\underline{\ ?\ }, \underline{\ ?\ })$

**4.** $\overrightarrow{CD} = (\underline{\ ?\ }, \underline{\ ?\ })$

**5.** $\overrightarrow{EF} = (\underline{\ ?\ }, \underline{\ ?\ })$

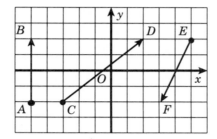

3. _____ (4)

4. _____ (4)

5. _____ (4)

Find the magnitude of each vector.

**6.** $\overrightarrow{GH} = (4, 3)$     **7.** $\overrightarrow{IJ} = (0, -8)$     **8.** $\overrightarrow{KL} = (-2, 10)$

6. _____ (4)

7. _____ (4)

8. _____ (4)

State whether the vectors are *parallel*, *perpendicular*, or *neither*.

**9.** $\overrightarrow{AB} = (9, -12)$     **10.** $\overrightarrow{RS} = (4, -6)$     **11.** $\overrightarrow{WX} = (10, 8)$
   $\overrightarrow{CD} = (-6, 8)$          $\overrightarrow{TU} = (6, -8)$          $\overrightarrow{YZ} = (-4, 5)$

9. _____ (5)

10. _____ (5)

11. _____ (5)

In Questions 12–15, $\overrightarrow{PQ} = (3, 4)$, $\overrightarrow{QR} = (2, -3)$, and $\overrightarrow{PR} = (5, 1)$. Write each answer as an ordered pair.

**12.** $\overrightarrow{PQ} + \overrightarrow{QR} = (\underline{\ ?\ }, \underline{\ ?\ })$     **13.** $\overrightarrow{PQ} + \overrightarrow{PR} = (\underline{\ ?\ }, \underline{\ ?\ })$

**14.** $3\overrightarrow{QR} = (\underline{\ ?\ }, \underline{\ ?\ })$     **15.** $\overrightarrow{PQ} + 2\overrightarrow{PR} = (\underline{\ ?\ }, \underline{\ ?\ })$

12. _____ (4)

13. _____ (4)

14. _____ (5)

15. _____ (5)

In Questions 16–18, find the coordinates of the midpoint of the segment that joins the two points.

**16.** $(5, 3)$ and $(9, 1)$     **17.** $(-6, 3)$ and $(2, -4)$

**18.** $(a, b)$ and $(a + 2, 3b)$

16. _____ (5)

17. _____ (5)

18. _____ (5)

**19.** $M$ is the midpoint of $\overline{AB}$. The coordinates of $M$ are $(1, 3)$ and the coordinates of $A$ are $(5, -3)$. Find the coordinates of $B$.

**20.** $E(0, 3)$, $F(4, 5)$, $G(8, 2)$, and $H(-2, -3)$ are the vertices of trapezoid *EFGH*. $\overline{EF}$ is a base. Find the coordinates of the endpoints of the median.

**21.** $J(-3, -1)$, $K(-1, 5)$, $L(7, 7)$, and $M(5, 1)$ are the vertices of parallelogram *JKLM*. Find the coordinates of the point of intersection of the diagonals.

19. _____ (6)

20. _____ (6)

21. _____ (5)

TESTS for GEOMETRY

NAME _____ DATE _____ SCORE _____

# Test 53  *Supplementary Test*

**Directions:** Write answers in the spaces provided.

Find the *x*- and *y*-intercepts of each line.

**1.** $4x + y = -20$

**2.** $6x - 8y = 30$

Find the slope and the *y*-intercept of each line.

**3.** $y = 5x - 4$

**4.** $y = \frac{3}{7}x$

**5.** $3x + 2y = 12$

**6.** $2x - 5y = 8$

In Questions 7 and 8, write the equation in point-slope form of the line described.

**7.** Slope $= -\frac{2}{5}$; passes through $(3, 7)$ _____

**8.** Passes through $(5, -1)$ and $(2, 3)$ _____

**9.** Line *k* has slope $\frac{3}{4}$ and passes through $(0, 2)$. Write an equation of *k* in slope-intercept form.

**10.** Given the line whose equation is $y - 3 = -\frac{3}{2}(x + 1)$, write the equation in standard form.

**11.** Use algebra to find the intersection of the lines $x + 2y = 5$ and $3x - y = 1$.

**12.** Determine whether the lines $3x + 4y = 12$ and $12x - 9y = 10$ are *parallel*, *perpendicular*, or *neither*.

**13.** Write an equation in point-slope form of the line perpendicular to the line $y = \frac{3}{5}x + 7$ and passing through the point $(-2, 5)$.

**14.** Write an equation in slope-intercept form of the line parallel to the line $2x - 5y = 7$ and passing through the point $(0, -4)$.

**15.** Write an equation in point-slope form of the perpendicular bisector of the segment joining $(2, 3)$ and $(10, 7)$.

**16.** Graph the line $2x - y = 3$ on the axes at the right.

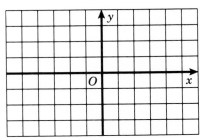

**Answers**

1. _____ (5)

2. _____ (5)

3. _____ (5)

4. _____ (5)

5. _____ (5)

6. _____ (5)

7. (See question) _____ (7)

8. (See question) _____ (7)

9. _____ (7)

10. _____ (7)

11. _____ (7)

12. _____ (7)

13. _____ (7)

14. _____ (7)

15. _____ (7)

16. (See question) _____ (7)

# Test 54  Lines and Coordinate Geometry Proofs

**Lessons 13-8, 13-9**

**Directions:** Write answers in the spaces provided.

In Questions 1–5, *ABCD* is a parallelogram.

1. Supply the coordinates of *C* without introducing new letters.

2. The midpoint of $\overline{AC}$ is $\left(\dfrac{?\,+\,?}{2},\ \dfrac{?\,+\,?}{2}\right)$.

3. The midpoint of $\overline{BD}$ is $\left(\dfrac{?\,+\,?}{2},\ \dfrac{?\,+\,?}{2}\right)$.

4. What is true about the midpoints of $\overline{AC}$ and $\overline{BD}$?

5. Therefore, the diagonals of a parallelogram __?__ .

Questions 1–5

In Questions 6–10, *KLMN* is an isosceles trapezoid.

6. Supply the coordinates of *M* without introducing new letters.

7. $KM = \sqrt{(?\,-\,?)^2 + (?\,-\,?)^2}$

8. $LN = \sqrt{(?\,-\,?)^2 + (?\,-\,?)^2}$

9. Is $KM = LN$?

10. Therefore, the diagonals of an isosceles trapezoid __?__ .

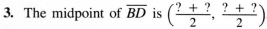

Questions 6–10

In Questions 11–13, $\triangle ABC \cong \triangle DEF$. Supply the coordinates of each point without introducing new letters.

11. *D*

12. *E*

13. *F*

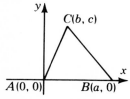
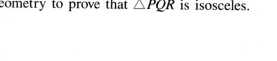

14. Use coordinate geometry to prove that $\triangle PQR$ is isosceles.

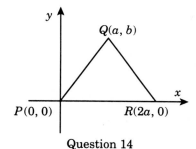

Question 14

15. Use coordinate geometry to prove that $\triangle DEF$ in the diagram is a right triangle.

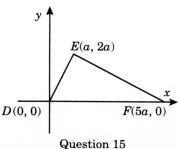

Question 15

**Answers**

1. _____ (6)

2. _____ (6)

3. _____ (6)

4. _____ (6)

5. _____ (6)

6. _____ (6)

7. _____ (6)

8. _____ (6)

9. _____ (6)

10. _____ (6)

11. _____ (6)

12. _____ (6)

13. _____ (6)

14. (See question) _____ (10)

15. (See question) _____ (12)

TESTS for GEOMETRY

● **Test 55** *Chapter 13 Test*

**Directions:** Write answers in the spaces provided.

Find the distance between the points named.

**1.** $(7, 3)$ and $(-2, 3)$        **2.** $(2, -4)$ and $(-1, 3)$

Find the center and radius of each circle.

**3.** $(x + 1)^2 + (y - 5)^2 = 4$

**4.** $(x - 3)^2 + y^2 = 10$

Write an equation of each circle described.

**5.** Center $(7, -3)$ and radius 6 _____

**6.** Center $(0, 4)$ and passes through $(1, -1)$ _____

Find the coordinates of the midpoint of the segment that joins the given points.

**7.** $(0, 9)$ and $(-4, 3)$        **8.** $(n, 2n)$ and $(-n, 6)$

Find the slope of the line through the points named. If the slope is not defined, write *not defined*.

**9.** $(4, -1)$; $(-2, -1)$

**10.** $(1, 1)$; $(3, 10)$

**11.** $(-3, 1)$; $(7, -1)$

In Questions 12 and 13, *ABCD* is a rhombus.

**12.** If the slope of $\overline{AB}$ is $\frac{2}{3}$, then the slope of $\overline{DC}$ is __?__ .

**13.** If the slope of $\overline{AC}$ is $\frac{9}{5}$, then the slope of $\overline{BD}$ is __?__ .

**14.** Line $l$ has slope $-\frac{5}{3}$ and passes through $(0, 1)$. Write an equation of $l$ in slope-intercept form.

In Questions 15 and 16, write an equation in point-slope form of the line described.

**15.** Slope $= \frac{1}{4}$; passes through $(5, 1)$

**16.** The perpendicular bisector of $\overline{AB}$, given $A(7, 2)$ and $B(5, 6)$

**Answers**

1. _____ (4)

2. _____ (4)

3. _____ (4)

4. _____ (4)

5. (See question) _____ (4)

6. (See question) _____ (5)

7. _____ (4)

8. _____ (4)

9. _____ (4)

10. _____ (4)

11. _____ (4)

12. _____ (4)

13. _____ (4)

14. _____ (4)

15. _____ (4)

16. _____ (5)

*(continued)*

## Test 55 *(continued)*

**17.** Find the point of intersection of the lines whose equations are
$x - 2y = 4$ and $3x + 2y = 4$.

In Questions 18–22, $\overrightarrow{AB} = (4, 6)$, $\overrightarrow{CD} = (-6, -9)$, $\overrightarrow{EF} = (3, -2)$,
and $\overrightarrow{FG} = (5, 12)$.

**18.** $|\overrightarrow{AB}| = \underline{\;?\;}$

**19.** $\overrightarrow{EF} + \overrightarrow{FG} = (\underline{\;?\;}, \underline{\;?\;})$

**20.** $3\overrightarrow{CD} = (\underline{\;?\;}, \underline{\;?\;})$

**21.** Determine whether $\overrightarrow{AB}$ and $\overrightarrow{CD}$ are *parallel*, *perpendicular*, or *neither*.

**22.** Determine whether $\overrightarrow{AB}$ and $\overrightarrow{EF}$ are *parallel*, *perpendicular*, or *neither*.

**23.** Graph the equation $x + 2y = 6$ on the given axes at the right.

**24.** Given *ABCD* is a parallelogram, choose and label appropriate coordinates for *A*, *B*, *C*, and *D*, and prove that the opposite sides of *ABCD* are congruent.

**Answers**

17. _____ (4)

18. _____ (3)

19. _____ (3)

20. _____ (3)

21. _____ (3)

22. _____ (3)

23. (See question) ____ (5)

24. (See question) ____ (10)

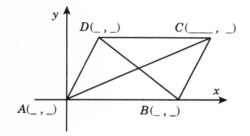

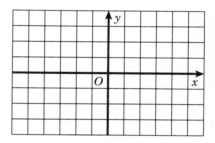

Question 23

### CHALLENGE (Optional)

$\triangle ABC$ has vertices $A(-5, -2)$, $B(7, -5)$, and $C(3, 1)$. Find the coordinates of the intersection of the three altitudes.

**ANSWER**

_____

# Test 56 *Supplementary Test*

**Directions:** Write answers in the spaces provided.

In Questions 1–6, use the transformation $S:(x, y) \rightarrow (x - 1, 2y)$. $A'$ and $B'$ are the images of points $A(2, 1)$ and $B(2, 3)$ under the transformation.

1. What is the image of $(4, 3)$?   2. What is the preimage of $(2, -2)$?

3. What is the distance $AB$?   4. What is the distance $A'B'$?

5. Is $S$ a one-to-one mapping?   6. Is $S$ an isometry?

Draw and label the image of each figure determined by the given reflection.

7. $R_x : \overline{CD} \rightarrow \overline{C'D'}$

8. $R_y : \overline{MN} \rightarrow \overline{M'N'}$

9. $R_t : \triangle RST \rightarrow \triangle R'S'T'$

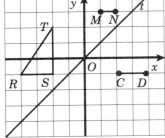

In Questions 10–14, use the translations $P:(x, y) \rightarrow (x + 3, y + 2)$ and $Q:(x, y) \rightarrow (x - 2, y + 4)$.

10. $P:(3, 5) \rightarrow (\underline{?}, \underline{?})$   11. $Q:(2, -4) \rightarrow (\underline{?}, \underline{?})$

12. If $P$ maps point $R$ to $R'$ and $Q$ maps $R'$ to $R''$, then the translation $T$ that maps $R$ to $R''$ is described as $T:(x, y) \rightarrow (\underline{?}, \underline{?})$.

13. The glide reflection determined by translation $P$ followed by a reflection in the $y$-axis maps $(x, y)$ to $(\underline{?}, \underline{?})$.

14. The glide reflection determined by translation $Q$ followed by a reflection in the $x$-axis maps $(x, y)$ to $(\underline{?}, \underline{?})$.

15. The glide reflection described by translation $G:(x, y) \rightarrow (x + 2, y + 2)$ and reflection in the line $y = x$ maps square $ABCD$ to $A'B'C'D'$.
    a. Is $A'B'C'D'$ a square?
    b. If the area of $ABCD$ is 9, can the area of $A'B'C'D'$ be determined? If so, what is the area of $A'B'C'D'$?

16. A museum plans to install a security system that operates on a reflected light beam. To protect both entrances to the main gallery, the transmitter is placed at $T$ and the receiver is placed at $R$. Using the grid, accurately determine where the reflectors on walls $A$ and $B$ must be placed so that the beam is transmitted to the receiver.

**Answers**

1. _____ (5)

2. _____ (5)

3. _____ (6)

4. _____ (6)

5. _____ (5)

6. _____ (6)

7. (See question) _____ (6)

8. (See question) _____ (6)

9. (See question) _____ (7)

10. _____ (5)

11. _____ (5)

12. _____ (6)

13. _____ (6)

14. _____ (6)

15. a. _____ (5)

  b. _____ (6)

16. (See question) _____ (9)

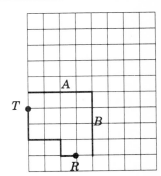

# Test 57   *Some Basic Mappings*

Lessons 14-1 through 14-5

**Directions:** Write answers in the spaces provided.

**Answers**

1. If $f(x) = 5x - 12$, find the image of 7 and the preimage of 13.

2. If $S:(x, y) \rightarrow (2x, y + 4)$, find the image of $(2, -3)$ and the preimage of $(9, 0)$.

3. If translation $T:(-4, 6) \rightarrow (11, 4)$, then $T:(x, y) \rightarrow (\underline{\ ?\ }, \underline{\ ?\ })$.

4. $D_{O, 3}:\overline{AB} \rightarrow \overline{A'B'}$. If $AB = 5$, then $A'B' = \underline{\ ?\ }$.

In Questions 5–8, classify each statement as true or false.

5. An isometry maps any figure to a similar figure but not necessarily a congruent figure.

6. $R_f$ is the notation for a rotation about the point $f$.

7. A glide followed by a reflection in a line parallel to the glide yields a glide reflection.

8. The dilation described by $D_{O, -4}$ is a contraction.

In Questions 9–11, *ABCD* is a square. *E, F, G,* and *H* are midpoints, as shown.

9. $D_{C, \frac{1}{2}}:A \rightarrow \underline{\ ?\ }$

10. $D_{J, -1}:C \rightarrow \underline{\ ?\ }$

11. $D_{A, 2}:\overline{EJ} \rightarrow \underline{\ ?\ }$

The figure consists of eight congruent 45°-45°-90° triangles. Write the image of each point under the given rotation or half-turn.

12. $\mathscr{R}_{O, 90}:G \rightarrow \underline{\ ?\ }$

13. $\mathscr{R}_{O, 45}:S \rightarrow \underline{\ ?\ }$

14. $H_O:D \rightarrow \underline{\ ?\ }$

15. $\mathscr{R}_{O, -135}:W \rightarrow \underline{\ ?\ }$

16. $\mathscr{R}_{O, 315}:F \rightarrow \underline{\ ?\ }$

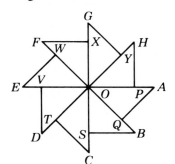

Questions 12–16

In Questions 17 and 18, use the axes at the right.

17. $D_{O, \frac{1}{2}}:\triangle RST \rightarrow \triangle R'S'T'$. Draw and label $\triangle R'S'T'$.

18. $\mathscr{R}_{O, 90}:\triangle RST \rightarrow \triangle R''S''T''$. Draw and label $\triangle R''S''T''$.

| Answers | |
|---|---|
| 1. _____ | (5) |
| 2. _____ | (5) |
| 3. _____ | (5) |
| 4. _____ | (5) |
| 5. _____ | (5) |
| 6. _____ | (5) |
| 7. _____ | (5) |
| 8. _____ | (5) |
| 9. _____ | (5) |
| 10. _____ | (5) |
| 11. _____ | (6) |
| 12. _____ | (6) |
| 13. _____ | (6) |
| 14. _____ | (6) |
| 15. _____ | (6) |
| 16. _____ | (6) |
| 17. (See question) | (7) |
| 18. (See question) | (7) |

# Test 58   *Composition and Symmetry*

**Lessons 14-6 through 14-8**

**Directions:** Write answers in the spaces provided.

Use the figure to complete
each statement.

1. $R_y \circ R_x : B \to \underline{\ ?\ }$

2. $\mathcal{R}_{O,\,90} \circ R_y : F \to \underline{\ ?\ }$

3. $R_y \circ H_O : E \to \underline{\ ?\ }$

4. $H_O \circ \mathcal{R}_{O,\,90} : C \to \underline{\ ?\ }$

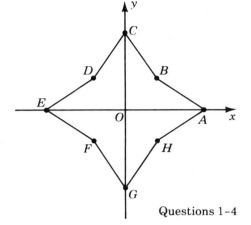

Questions 1–4

**Answers**

1. _____ (5)

2. _____ (5)

3. _____ (5)

4. _____ (5)

5. _____ (4)

6. _____ (4)

7. _____ (4)

8. _____ (4)

9. _____ (4)

10. _____ (4)

11. _____ (5)

12. _____ (5)

13. _____ (5)

14. _____ (5)

In Questions 5–8, complete each statement. $I$ is the identity
transformation.

5. $S \circ I = \underline{\ ?\ }$

6. $S^{-1} \circ S = \underline{\ ?\ }$

7. $I \circ S^{-1} = \underline{\ ?\ }$

8. $I \circ I = \underline{\ ?\ }$

9. Given a rule for a mapping $S : (x, y) \to (x - 2, 2y)$, write the rule
   for $S^{-1}$.

10. If dilation $D$ with center at origin $O$ maps $(2, 5)$ to $(6, 15)$, then
    $D^{-1}$ maps $(12, -9)$ to $(\underline{\ ?\ }, \underline{\ ?\ })$.

Given point $E(4, 2)$ and origin $O$. Use the graph to find the coordinates
of each image point.

11. $R_y \circ R_x : (4, 2) \to (\underline{\ ?\ }, \underline{\ ?\ })$

12. $H_O \circ H_E : (4, 3) \to (\underline{\ ?\ }, \underline{\ ?\ })$

13. $R_x \circ D_{O,\,-2} : (-1, 3) \to (\underline{\ ?\ }, \underline{\ ?\ })$

14. $R_y \circ \mathcal{R}_{E,\,90} : (4, 1) \to (\underline{\ ?\ }, \underline{\ ?\ })$

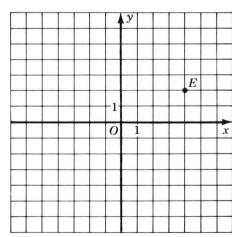

*(continued)*

**SHEET 87**

## Test 58 *(continued)*

In Questions 15–17, *ABCD* is an isosceles trapezoid.

**15.** Name a line of symmetry for *ABCD*.

**16.** Does *ABCD* have point symmetry?

**17.** Does *ABCD* have rotational symmetry other than 0° and 360°?

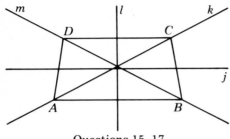

Questions 15–17

**Answers**

15. _____ (3)

16. _____ (3)

17. _____ (3)

18. _____ (3)

19. _____ (3)

20. _____ (3)

21. (See question) ___ (9)

22. (See question) ___ (9)

**18.** How many symmetry lines does the figure at the right have?

**19.** Does the figure have point symmetry?

**20.** Which of the following is *not* a rotational symmetry for the figure?

(A) $\mathcal{R}_{O,\,45}$   (B) $\mathcal{R}_{O,\,90}$   (C) $\mathcal{R}_{O,\,180}$   (D) $\mathcal{R}_{O,\,270}$

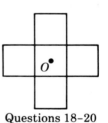

Questions 18–20

In Questions 21 and 22, use the translation $T:(x,\,y) \rightarrow (x - 4,\, y + 1)$.

**21.** Draw and label the image $\triangle A'B'C'$ of $\triangle ABC$ under $T \circ R_x$.

**22.** Draw and label the image $\triangle A'B'C'$ of $\triangle ABC$ under $R_x \circ T$.

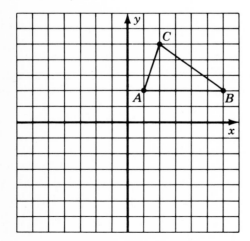

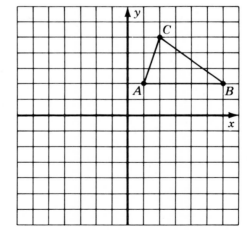

# Test 59 *Chapter 14 Test*

**Directions:** Write answers in the spaces provided.

In Questions 1–4, use the transformations $T:(x, y) \rightarrow (x + 2, y - 1)$ and $S:(x, y) \rightarrow (2x, y)$.

**1.** Find $T:(-1, 4)$.

**2.** Find $S:(3, 5)$.

**3.** What is the preimage of $(4, -1)$ under $T$?

**4.** Which is an isometry?

   **(A)** $T$     **(B)** $S$     **(C)** both $T$ and $S$     **(D)** neither $T$ nor $S$

Use the figure to complete each statement.

**5.** $S:(x, y) \rightarrow (-x, -y)$. $S:F \rightarrow \underline{?}$

**6.** $T:(x, y) \rightarrow (x + 2, y - 1)$. $T:L \rightarrow \underline{?}$

**7.** $R_y:J \rightarrow \underline{?}$

**8.** $R_x:B \rightarrow \underline{?}$

**9.** $R_j:Q \rightarrow \underline{?}$

**10.** $\mathcal{R}_{O, 90}:C \rightarrow \underline{?}$

**11.** $\mathcal{R}_{O, 180}:N \rightarrow \underline{?}$

**12.** $H_O:K \rightarrow \underline{?}$

**13.** $H_C:B \rightarrow \underline{?}$

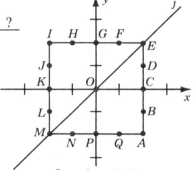

Questions 5–13

In Questions 14–20, use $T:(x, y) \rightarrow (x - 1, y + 2)$, $P(2, 3)$, origin $O$, and line $l$ with equation $y = x$. Use the given graph to complete each statement.

**14.** $R_x \circ R_y:(2, 3) \rightarrow (\underline{?}, \underline{?})$

**15.** $T \circ R_x:(4, 2) \rightarrow (\underline{?}, \underline{?})$

**16.** $H_P \circ R_y:(2, 5) \rightarrow (\underline{?}, \underline{?})$

**17.** $H_O \circ H_P:(-1, 4) \rightarrow (\underline{?}, \underline{?})$

**18.** $R_y \circ R_l:(2, 3) \rightarrow (\underline{?}, \underline{?})$

**19.** $R_y \circ R_l = \mathcal{R}_{\underline{?}, \underline{?}}$

**20.** $R_x \circ D_{O, \frac{1}{2}}:(6, 2) \rightarrow (\underline{?}, \underline{?})$

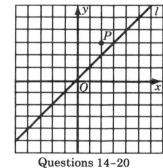

Questions 14–20

| | | |
|---|---|---|
| 1. _____ | (2) |
| 2. _____ | (2) |
| 3. _____ | (2) |
| 4. _____ | (2) |
| 5. _____ | (2) |
| 6. _____ | (2) |
| 7. _____ | (2) |
| 8. _____ | (2) |
| 9. _____ | (2) |
| 10. _____ | (2) |
| 11. _____ | (2) |
| 12. _____ | (2) |
| 13. _____ | (2) |
| 14. _____ | (5) |
| 15. _____ | (5) |
| 16. _____ | (5) |
| 17. _____ | (5) |
| 18. _____ | (5) |
| 19. _____ | (5) |
| 20. _____ | (5) |

*(continued)*

## Test 59 *(continued)*

| | Answers |
|---|---|
| In Questions 21 and 22, *I* is the identity transformation. | 21. _____ (2) |
| **21.** $I \circ R_x = \underline{\ ?\ }$ | 22. _____ (2) |
| **22.** $T \circ T^{-1} = \underline{\ ?\ }$ | 23. a. _____ (2) |

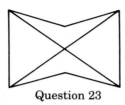

Question 23

**23. a.** Does the figure at the right have point symmetry?
 **b.** How many symmetry lines does the figure have?

Answers continued:
23. b. _____ (2)
24. (See question) _____ (8)
25. (See question) _____ (7)
26. _____ (4)
27. _____ (4)
28. _____ (4)
29. _____ (4)

**24.** Given $T:(x, y) \rightarrow (x + 2, y + 1)$. Draw and label the image $\triangle A'B'C'$ of $\triangle ABC$ by $R_x \circ T$.

**25.** Draw and label the image $\triangle D'E'F'$ of $\triangle DEF$ by $D_{O, -2}$.

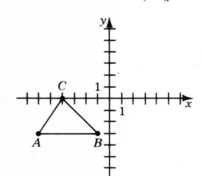

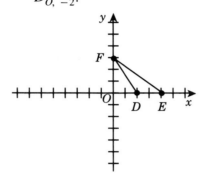

$\overline{WS}$ bisects $\angle VOZ$ and $\overline{OR} \cong \overline{OS} \cong \overline{OT} \cong \overline{OV} \cong \overline{OW} \cong \overline{OZ}$.
Find the image under each composite.

**26.** $R_y \circ \mathcal{R}_{O, 90}:V \rightarrow \underline{\ ?\ }$

**27.** $H_O \circ \mathcal{R}_{O, 45}:W \rightarrow \underline{\ ?\ }$

**28.** $\mathcal{R}_{O, 135} \circ R_y:Z \rightarrow \underline{\ ?\ }$

**29.** $\mathcal{R}_{O, 135} \circ H_O:T \rightarrow \underline{\ ?\ }$

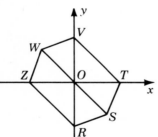

Questions 26–29

### CHALLENGE (Optional)

Given $T:(x, y) \rightarrow (x - 3, y - 2)$ and points $A(1, 3)$, $B(8, 3)$, $C(6, 5)$, and $D(3, 5)$.

Draw and label the image $A'B'C'D'$ of $ABCD$ under the composite $\mathcal{R}_{O, -90} \circ R_x \circ T \circ D_{A, \frac{3}{2}}$.

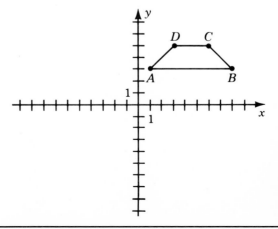

# Test 60   *Cumulative Test, Chapters 13–14*

**Answers**

**Directions:** Write answers in the spaces provided.

In Questions 1–3, supply the letter of the equation that is named at the left.

1. Point-slope form

2. Slope-intercept form

3. Standard form

 (A) $y = mx + b$
 (B) $y - y_1 = m(x - x_1)$
 (C) $By = Ax + C$
 (D) $x - x_1 = m(y - y_1)$
 (E) $Ax + By = C$

4. Find the distance between the points with coordinates $(-5, 2)$ and $(7, 7)$.

In Questions 5–7, write an equation of the circle described.

5. Center $(3, -2)$ and radius 7 _____

6. Center $(0, 3)$ and passing through $(5, 1)$ _____

7. Center at the origin and congruent to the circle $(x - 5)^2 + (y - 4)^2 = 16$

In Questions 8–10, find the slope of each line described.

8. The line that passes through $(5, 6)$ and $(-1, 2)$

9. The line $4x - 2y = 7$

10. The line $y = -\dfrac{5}{8}x + 2$

11. Write an equation in slope-intercept form of the line that passes through $(0, 7)$ and is parallel to $y = \dfrac{2}{3}x - 4$.

12. Write an equation in point-slope form of the line that passes through $(1, -2)$ and is perpendicular to $y = \dfrac{2}{3}x - 4$.

13. The slope of a horizontal line is _____?_____ .
 *(not defined, zero)*

14. Find the coordinates of the midpoint of the segment that joins the points $(8, 12)$ and $(-2, 5)$.

15. Graph the line $3x - 4y = 12$ on the axes at the right.

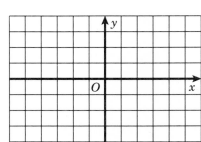

**Answers**

1. _____ (2)

2. _____ (2)

3. _____ (2)

4. _____ (3)

5. (See question) _____ (2)

6. (See question) _____ (2)

7. _____ (2)

8. _____ (2)

9. _____ (2)

10. _____ (2)

11. _____ (2)

12. _____ (2)

13. _____ (2)

14. _____ (2)

15. (See question) _____ (3)

*(continued)*

## Test 60 *(continued)*

In Questions 16 and 17, state whether the lines are *parallel*, *perpendicular*, or *neither*.

**16.** $3x + 4y = 15$
$12x - 9y = 12$

**17.** $4x + 6y = 12$
$6x + 9y = -12$

**18.** Given points $A(-3, 8)$ and $B(2, -4)$.
    **a.** $\overrightarrow{AB} = (\underline{\ ?\ }, \underline{\ ?\ })$
    **b.** $|\overrightarrow{AB}| = \underline{\ ?\ }$

In Questions 19–21, $\overrightarrow{PQ} = (6, 9)$, $\overrightarrow{QR} = (-6, 4)$, $\overrightarrow{RS} = (-8, -12)$, and $\overrightarrow{TU} = (-4, 3)$.

**19.** Tell whether each pair of vectors is *parallel*, *perpendicular*, or *neither*.
    **a.** $\overrightarrow{PQ}$ and $\overrightarrow{QR}$     **b.** $\overrightarrow{PQ}$ and $\overrightarrow{RS}$     **c.** $\overrightarrow{PQ}$ and $\overrightarrow{TU}$

**20.** $\overrightarrow{PQ} + \overrightarrow{QR} = (\underline{\ ?\ }, \underline{\ ?\ })$

**21.** $2\overrightarrow{QR} + \overrightarrow{RS} = (\underline{\ ?\ }, \underline{\ ?\ })$

**22.** Use algebra to find the intersection of the lines $3x + y = 7$ and $2x - 3y = -10$.

In Questions 23–26, use the transformations $G:(x, y) \rightarrow (x - 2, y + 1)$ and $H:(x, y) \rightarrow (2x, y + 1)$.

**23.** $G:(-3, 1) \rightarrow (\underline{\ ?\ }, \underline{\ ?\ })$     **24.** $H:(\underline{\ ?\ }, \underline{\ ?\ }) \rightarrow (8, 8)$

**25.** Which transformations are one-to-one mappings?
    **(A)** $G$ only   **(B)** $H$ only   **(C)** both $G$ and $H$   **(D)** neither $G$ nor $H$

**26.** Which transformations are isometries?
    **(A)** $G$ only   **(B)** $H$ only   **(C)** both $G$ and $H$   **(D)** neither $G$ nor $H$

Given the points $A(3, 6)$ and $B(2, -5)$.

**27.** Write the coordinates of the image of $A$ under reflection in the $y$-axis.

**28.** Write the coordinates of the image of $B$ under reflection in the $x$-axis.

**29.** Write the coordinates of the image of $A$ under reflection in the line $y = 2$.

**30.** Write the coordinates of the image of $B$ under reflection in the line $y = x$.

**Answers**

16. _____ (2)

17. _____ (2)

18. a. _____ (2)

   b. _____ (2)

19. a. _____ (2)

   b. _____ (2)

   c. _____ (2)

20. _____ (2)

21. _____ (2)

22. _____ (3)

23. _____ (2)

24. _____ (2)

25. _____ (2)

26. _____ (2)

27. _____ (2)

28. _____ (2)

29. _____ (2)

30. _____ (3)

*(continued)*

TESTS for GEOMETRY

## Test 60 *(continued)*

Given: $\overline{OB} \cong \overline{OE} \cong \overline{OG} \cong \overline{OJ}$; $C$, $D$, $H$, and $I$ are midpoints; $m \angle COA = m \angle DOF = 60$

**31.** $R_y{:}J \to$ __?__

**32.** $H_O{:}C \to$ __?__

**33.** $\mathcal{R}_{O,\,120}{:}H \to$ __?__

**34.** $\mathcal{R}_{O,\,60}{:}G \to$ __?__

**35.** $D_{O,\,-2}{:}C \to$ __?__

**36.** $R_y \circ H_C{:}O \to$ __?__

**37.** $\mathcal{R}_{O,\,180} \circ R_x{:}I \to$ __?__

**38.** $H_O \circ D_{G,\,3}{:}H \to$ __?__

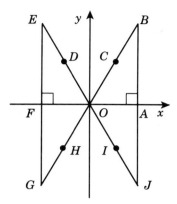

**39.** If $T{:}(x,\,y) \to (x+3,\,4y)$, then $T^{-1}{:}(x,\,y) \to (\underline{\;?\;},\,\underline{\;?\;})$.

**40.** Without introducing any new letters, supply coordinates for the points listed.
 **a.** $C\,(\underline{\;?\;},\,\underline{\;?\;})$
 **b.** $E\,(\underline{\;?\;},\,\underline{\;?\;})$

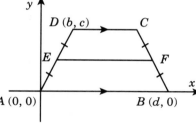

**41.** Let $M$ be the midpoint of the hypotenuse of right $\triangle ABC$. Use coordinate geometry to prove that $M$ is equidistant from the three vertices.

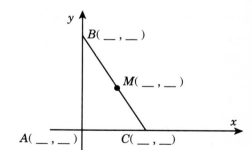

Answers

31. _____ (2)
32. _____ (2)
33. _____ (2)
34. _____ (2)
35. _____ (2)
36. _____ (2)
37. _____ (2)
38. _____ (2)
39. _____ (2)
40. a. _____ (2)
 b. _____ (2)
41. (See question) _____ (8)

NAME _____ DATE _____ SCORE _____

# Test 61  *Cumulative Test, Chapters 8–14*

Answers

**Directions:** Write answers in the spaces provided.

Indicate the best answer by writing the appropriate letter.

1. If $AB = 6$ and $BC = 8$, then $AC =$ __?__ .

   (A) 9          (B) $2\sqrt{7}$

   (C) 10         (D) $9\sqrt{5}$

2. If $m \angle A = 60$ and $AB = 5$, then $BC =$ __?__ .

   (A) $5\sqrt{3}$     (B) 10

   (C) $5\sqrt{2}$     (D) 5

Questions 1–5

3. If $m \angle DBC = 45$ and $BC = 7$, then $BD =$ __?__ .

   (A) $7\sqrt{3}$     (B) $\dfrac{7\sqrt{2}}{2}$     (C) $\dfrac{7\sqrt{3}}{3}$

   (D) 7          (E) $7\sqrt{2}$

4. In $\triangle ABC$, $\tan A =$ __?__ .

   (A) $\dfrac{BC}{AB}$     (B) $\dfrac{BC}{AC}$     (C) $\dfrac{AB}{AC}$     (D) $\dfrac{AC}{AB}$

5. In $\triangle ABC$, which proportions are true?

   I. $\dfrac{AB}{BD} = \dfrac{BD}{BC}$     II. $\dfrac{AD}{BD} = \dfrac{BD}{DC}$     III. $\dfrac{AD}{AB} = \dfrac{AB}{AC}$

   (A) I only          (B) II only          (C) III only

   (D) II and III      (E) none of these

6. A triangle with sides of lengths 8, 9, and 12 is a(n) __?__ triangle.

   (A) acute          (B) right          (C) obtuse

   (D) equiangular    (E) Answer cannot be determined.

7. In an equilateral triangle with sides of length 10, the length of the altitude to the base is __?__ .

   (A) 10          (B) 5          (C) $5\sqrt{2}$

   (D) $10\sqrt{3}$     (E) none of these

8. Using only the angle of elevation of the sun and the length of the shadow of a tree, which trigonometric function could be used to find the height of the tree?

   (A) sine          (B) cosine          (C) tangent

1. _____ (1)
2. _____ (1)
3. _____ (1)
4. _____ (1)
5. _____ (1)
6. _____ (1)
7. _____ (1)
8. _____ (1)

*(continued)*

TESTS for GEOMETRY

**Test 61** *(continued)*

**Answers**

9. A segment whose endpoints are points of a circle *must* be a __?__ and
can be a __?__ .

   **(A)** chord, secant     **(B)** diameter, radius
   **(C)** secant, chord     **(D)** chord, diameter

10. In circle *P*, if $m \angle E = 65$, then $m \angle C = $ __?__ .

    **(A)** 65      **(B)** 115      **(C)** 135
    **(D)** 130      **(E)** none of these

11. In circle *P*, which of the following segments must
be congruent?
    I. $\overline{BC}$ and $\overline{CD}$    II. $\overline{BC}$ and $\overline{DE}$
    III. $\overline{AB}$ and $\overline{AF}$    IV. $\overline{BP}$ and $\overline{PE}$

    **(A)** II and IV      **(B)** III and IV      **(C)** I, II, and III
    **(D)** II, III, and IV   **(E)** all of these

Questions 10, 11

9. _____ (2)

10. _____ (1)

11. _____ (2)

12. _____ (1)

13. _____ (1)

14. _____ (1)

15. _____ (2)

16. _____ (2)

17. _____ (2)

In Questions 12–16, *O* is the center of the circle, $m\widehat{AE} = 100$,
$m\widehat{AB} = 30$, and $m\widehat{BC} = 80$.

12. $m \angle 1 = $ __?__
    **(A)** 20      **(B)** 30      **(C)** 40
    **(D)** 50      **(E)** none of these

13. $m \angle 2 = $ __?__
    **(A)** 90      **(B)** 130      **(C)** 65
    **(D)** 60      **(E)** none of these

14. $m \angle 3 = $ __?__
    **(A)** 60      **(B)** 65      **(C)** 70
    **(D)** 90      **(E)** none of these

Questions 12–16

15. If $AF = 10$, $AD = 13$, and $CF = 5$, then $EF = $ __?__ .
    **(A)** 26      **(B)** 11      **(C)** 15
    **(D)** 6      **(E)** none of these

16. If $GC = 12$, $GB = 4$, and $GA = 3$, then $GD = $ __?__ .
    **(A)** $11\frac{2}{3}$      **(B)** $14\frac{2}{3}$      **(C)** 16
    **(D)** 9      **(E)** none of these

17. In circle *P* at the right, if $QS = 20$ and $US = 4$,
then $TR = $ __?__ .
    **(A)** 12      **(B)** 8      **(C)** 16
    **(D)** Answer cannot be determined.

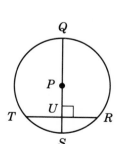

Question 17

## Test 61 (continued)

18. Using a compass and a straightedge only, it is *not* possible to construct an angle with measure equal to __?__ the measure of a given angle.

 (A) $\frac{1}{2}$  (B) $\frac{1}{4}$  (C) $\frac{1}{6}$

 (D) $\frac{3}{8}$  (E) none of these

19. To construct a circle circumscribed about a given triangle, you must first construct two __?__ .

 (A) medians  (B) angle bisectors  (C) perpendicular bisectors
 (D) altitudes  (E) none of these

20. In a plane, the locus of points 3 cm from a given point is __?__ .

 (A) a line  (B) a circle  (C) a point
 (D) two points  (E) none of these

21. In space, the locus of points equidistant from two parallel lines is a __?__ .

 (A) point  (B) line  (C) pair of parallel lines
 (D) plane  (E) none of these

22. The lines containing which of the following are always concurrent at a point *inside* any triangle?
 I. the medians  II. the perpendicular bisectors of the sides
 III. the altitudes  IV. the bisectors of the angles

 (A) I only  (B) II only  (C) III only
 (D) IV only  (E) I and IV only

23. In a circle with radius 12 and $m\widehat{AB} = 120$, the length of $\widehat{AB}$ = __?__ .

 (A) $48\pi$  (B) $12\pi$  (C) $16\pi$
 (D) $8\pi$  (E) none of these

24. The area of a regular polygon with perimeter 48 and apothem $4\sqrt{3}$ is __?__ .

 (A) $192\sqrt{3}$  (B) $64\sqrt{3}$  (C) $96\sqrt{3}$
 (D) $48\sqrt{3}$  (E) none of these

25. If the ratio of the lengths of the corresponding sides of two similar polygons is $2:3$, then the ratio of their areas is __?__ .

 (A) $8:27$  (B) $4:6$  (C) $2:3$
 (D) $4:9$  (E) none of these

26. The area of a 45°-45°-90° triangle with one leg of length 8 is __?__ .

 (A) 16  (B) 32  (C) $32\sqrt{2}$
 (D) 64  (E) none of these

18. _____ (2)

19. _____ (2)

20. _____ (2)

21. _____ (2)

22. _____ (2)

23. _____ (2)

24. _____ (2)

25. _____ (2)

26. _____ (2)

*(continued)*

TESTS for GEOMETRY

## Test 61 *(continued)*

**Answers**

27. $\pi$ is the ratio of the _?_ of a circle to its _?_ .

   **(A)** area, circumference      **(B)** diameter, circumference
   **(C)** circumference, diameter      **(D)** circumference, radius

28. The area of a circle with radius 10 is _?_ .

   **(A)** $100\pi$      **(B)** $200\pi$      **(C)** $20\pi$
   **(D)** $40\pi$      **(E)** none of these

29. The area of a trapezoid with height 10 and bases 9 and 13 is _?_ .

   **(A)** 55      **(B)** 220      **(C)** 110
   **(D)** $27\frac{1}{2}$      **(E)** none of these

30. A square is inscribed in a circle of radius 10. What is the area of the square?

   **(A)** 100      **(B)** 200      **(C)** 400
   **(D)** $100\sqrt{2}$      **(E)** none of these

31. One side of a rectangle has length 12 and the rectangle has area 60. What is its perimeter?

   **(A)** 17      **(B)** 30      **(C)** 34
   **(D)** 36      **(E)** none of these

32. A sphere with radius 6 has an area of _?_ .

   **(A)** $36\pi$      **(B)** $144\pi$      **(C)** $216\pi$
   **(D)** $288\pi$      **(E)** none of these

33. The lateral area of a regular hexagonal prism with base edge 5 and height 10 is _?_ .

   **(A)** 250      **(B)** 300      **(C)** 400
   **(D)** 500      **(E)** none of these

34. The regular square pyramid shown has slant height _?_ .

   **(A)** $4\sqrt{61}$      **(B)** $2\sqrt{11}$      **(C)** $\sqrt{194}$      **(D)** 13

35. The regular square pyramid shown has volume _?_ .

   **(A)** 200      **(B)** 400      **(C)** 600      **(D)** 800

36. The bases of a right prism are congruent to the base of the given pyramid. If the volume of the prism is equal to that of the pyramid, then the height of the prism is _?_ .

   **(A)** 2      **(B)** 3      **(C)** 4      **(D)** 6

27. _____ (2)

28. _____ (2)

29. _____ (2)

30. _____ (2)

31. _____ (2)

32. _____ (2)

33. _____ (2)

34. _____ (2)

35. _____ (2)

36. _____ (2)

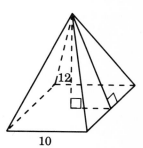

12

10

Questions 34–36

*(continued)*

## Test 61 *(continued)*

**37.** Two similar pyramids have heights of 4 and 10. The ratio of their volumes is __?__ .

    **(A)** $2:5$         **(B)** $6:15$         **(C)** $4:25$

    **(D)** $8:125$       **(E)** none of these

**38.** The total area of a right circular cone with radius 6 and height 8 is __?__ .

    **(A)** $84\pi$         **(B)** $60\pi$         **(C)** $96\pi$

    **(D)** $164\pi$      **(E)** none of these

**39.** Two similar pyramids have base edges of 6 and 9. If the total area of the smaller pyramid is 60, then the total area of the larger pyramid is __?__ .

    **(A)** 90         **(B)** 135         **(C)** 180

    **(D)** 240       **(E)** none of these

**40.** If the radius of a cone is tripled and the height is doubled, then the volume is multiplied by a factor of __?__ .

    **(A)** 5         **(B)** 6         **(C)** 8

    **(D)** 12       **(E)** 18

In Questions 41–46, use $A(0, 3)$, $B(4, 1)$, $C(-2, -1)$, $D(7, 7)$, and $E(1, -1)$.

**41.** $AD = $ __?__

    **(A)** 11     **(B)** $\sqrt{33}$     **(C)** $\sqrt{65}$     **(D)** 10

**42.** $\overrightarrow{AB} = $ __?__

    **(A)** $(4, 2)$     **(B)** $(-4, 2)$     **(C)** $(4, 4)$     **(D)** $(4, -2)$

**43.** $|\overrightarrow{DE}| = $ __?__

    **(A)** 10     **(B)** 14     **(C)** $6\sqrt{2}$     **(D)** $7\sqrt{2}$

**44.** Which pair of lines are perpendicular?

    **(A)** $\overleftrightarrow{AB}$ and $\overleftrightarrow{BC}$     **(B)** $\overleftrightarrow{AB}$ and $\overleftrightarrow{AC}$     **(C)** $\overleftrightarrow{AB}$ and $\overleftrightarrow{AD}$

    **(D)** $\overleftrightarrow{AC}$ and $\overleftrightarrow{BD}$     **(E)** none of these

**45.** An equation of $\overleftrightarrow{AC}$ in slope-intercept form is __?__ .

    **(A)** $y = 2x - 3$     **(B)** $y = 2x + 3$     **(C)** $y = \frac{1}{2}x + 3$

    **(D)** $y = -\frac{1}{2}x + 3$     **(E)** none of these

**46.** The midpoint of $\overline{DE}$ has coordinates __?__ .

    **(A)** $(3, 4)$         **(B)** $(4, 3)$         **(C)** $(3, 3)$

    **(D)** $(4, 4)$       **(E)** none of these

**Answers**

37. _____ (2)

38. _____ (2)

39. _____ (2)

40. _____ (2)

41. _____ (2)

42. _____ (2)

43. _____ (2)

44. _____ (2)

45. _____ (2)

46. _____ (2)

*(continued)*

TESTS for GEOMETRY

## Test 61 *(continued)*

47. The circle $(x - 3)^2 + (y + 2)^2 = 4$ has center ___?___ and radius ___?___ .

   **(A)** $(-3, 4), 4$      **(B)** $(3, -2), 4$      **(C)** $(-3, 2), 2$
   **(D)** $(3, -2), 2$      **(E)** none of these

48. An equation of the line through point $(4, 5)$ with slope $\frac{3}{4}$ is ___?___ .

   **(A)** $y = \frac{3}{4}x - 4$      **(B)** $y = \frac{3}{4}x - 3$      **(C)** $y = \frac{3}{4}x + 2$

   **(D)** $y = \frac{3}{4}x - 5$      **(E)** none of these

49. If $\overrightarrow{PQ} = (4, 6)$ and $\overrightarrow{QR} = (-2, 3)$, then $\overrightarrow{PQ} + 2\overrightarrow{QR} = $ ___?___ .

   **(A)** $(2, 3)$      **(B)** $(0, 12)$      **(C)** $(0, 9)$
   **(D)** $(8, 12)$      **(E)** none of these

50. If $T:(x, y) \to (2x, y - 6)$, then $T^{-1}:(x, y) \to$ ___?___ .

   **(A)** $(-2x, y - 6)$      **(B)** $(-2x, y + 6)$      **(C)** $(-\frac{1}{2}x, y + 6)$
   **(D)** $(\frac{1}{2}x, y + 6)$      **(E)** none of these

51. If $D_{O, 3}:\triangle ABC \to \triangle A'B'C'$, then the area of $\triangle A'B'C'$ is ___?___ times the area of $\triangle ABC$.

   **(A)** $2$      **(B)** $3$      **(C)** $6$
   **(D)** $9$      **(E)** none of these

In Questions 52–56, *ABCD* and *DEFG* are congruent squares.

52. $R_y:ABCD \to$ ___?___
   **(A)** *GDEF*      **(B)** *GFED*
   **(C)** *DEFG*      **(D)** *EFGD*

53. $R_x:GDEF \to$ ___?___
   **(A)** *ADCB*      **(B)** *GDEF*
   **(C)** *EDGF*      **(D)** *GFED*

54. $H_D:\overline{GF} \to$ ___?___
   **(A)** $\overline{CB}$      **(B)** $\overline{BC}$
   **(C)** $\overline{CD}$      **(D)** $\overline{DA}$

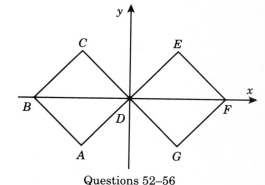

Questions 52–56

55. The single mapping that maps *ABCD* into *GDEF* is a ___?___ .
   **(A)** rotation      **(B)** reflection      **(C)** translation
   **(D)** dilation      **(E)** none of these

56. $R_x \circ \mathscr{R}_{D, 90}:E \to$ ___?___
   **(A)** *A*      **(B)** *G*      **(C)** *E*      **(D)** *C*

47. _____ (2)
48. _____ (2)
49. _____ (2)
50. _____ (2)
51. _____ (2)
52. _____ (2)
53. _____ (2)
54. _____ (2)
55. _____ (2)
56. _____ (2)